"I DON'T KNOW WHO YOU ARE ANYMORE"

A Family's Struggle with Depression

"I DON'T KNOW WHO YOU ARE ANYMORE"

A Family's Struggle with Depression

Kellie Branson
Dale Babcock, M.S.

Library of Congress Catalog Card Number
91-076568

International Standard Book Number 0-9625040-3-3

Cover Design and Typography:
K. Wynn Christensen
Laser Graphics
Meridian, Idaho

LEGENDARY PUBLISHING COMPANY
Lorry Roberts, Publisher
P.O. Box 7706
Boise, Idaho 83707-1706

DEDICATION

This book is dedicated to the millions of families worldwide struggling with depression every year.

PREFACE

This is a true story based on one family's struggle with depression and the perception of one family member. It should be noted that the ongoing situation of this family and of other families may be perceived differently by individual family members. Due to the nature of this illness and the stigma that still exists regarding it, some names have been changed. It was not the intention of the authors to criticize or hold up for ridicule any person suffering from depression. On the contrary, we have tried to emphasize that when a depressed person exhibits uncharacteristic behavior, it should be attributed to the effects of the illness and not as an indication of any defects or flaws in the depressed person's moral character.

The clinical information contained throughout the book is based on the writings, research and experiences of many mental health professionals around the country and from information gathered from materials provided by the National Institute of Mental Health.

The authors have tried to address events and situations that are common to many families struggling with depression and to offer some practical methods for coping that have proved helpful to others. We recognize that these may not be effective in every family situation.

Throughout the writing of this book, we constantly referred to it as "the light." It is our hope that it will shine a light into the lives of real families struggling with the darkness of depression and help to lead them out of the nightmare and into the dawn of a new way of living.

ACKNOWLEDGMENTS

The authors wish to acknowledge the mental health associations, hospitals, and clinicians from throughout the United States, and the staff at the National Institute of Mental Health for their assistance in providing information for this book.

We would also like to thank Jean Terra for her tireless work in the editing, and helping to structure the manuscript; to Lorry Roberts of Legendary Publishing Company for believing in the potential of this book; and to Wynn Christensen for graphics, typesetting, and his continued patience in the face of our many changes and rewrites.

We express our sincere appreciation to our families for all their help and support.

TABLE OF CONTENTS

INTRODUCTION

It seemed like the end of our world.

On a dark October night in 1986, my depressed husband attempted suicide.

It was a terrifying experience for our entire family. It was the reason we began our search for the answers to a problem that affects millions of American families every year.

To all appearances, we were a typical American family. We had just purchased our first home. With our two kids and a dog, our own business, and two cars in the garage, we seemed to have it all. We were living the great American dream.

But, for us, the dream suddenly became a nightmare that seemed to have no end. This book is the story of our family's struggle with depression.

Until my husband's depression was diagnosed, we did not know anything about depression. We knew even less about suicide. I thought being depressed was something you felt for an afternoon when you had "the blues."

We quickly learned that depression is a serious problem that by latest government estimates affects millions of people in the United States every year. Depression begins as an individual problem but it eventually affects the entire family. The number of family members coping with the effects of this debilitating illness is astronomical.

Our family was lucky. We sought help and we found it. Together, we learned how to cope with our problem and we discovered some new ways of putting our family back together again.

This book is the story of our journey through the darkness of depression into the light of hope and on to a new life for all of us. Our journey began with a telephone call to a crisis hotline in a moment of deepest despair. That call led us to a therapist, Dale Babcock, who specialized in family counseling. He warned us that overcoming depression would be one of the most difficult things we would ever do in our lives. He was right.

Dale said he would be there to provide direction, support and encouragement for our family when the therapy got tough.

The therapy did get tough and he was there.

Our family started therapy as a team with Dale as the coach. He taught us, listened to us, watched and encouraged us as we won and lost and then won again in the depression game.

He never gave up on us, and he would not allow us to give up on ourselves. We were all in the game together and we were determined to win.

We did succeed in making it through the darkest hours and much of the credit goes to our coach, who provided the insight, inspiration, and the game plans that brought us to a more rewarding and enriching life for our family.

We have teamed up again to write this book. Not only does our book tell the story of our family's struggle with depression, it also provides a therapist's expertise in the communication and relationship problems that plague almost every family affected with this illness.

The stigma surrounding mental illness is still alive and well. Because it is the kind of thing that "we just don't talk about," there has been very little written on depression from a family perspective. The problem is that as long as we keep depression in the closet and no one finds out how it has affected our family, the longer we will go on living in the hell it creates, alone.

This book provides useful information for other families living with depression. Families are often the victims of psychological terrorism, verbal abuse and physical battering inflicted on them by the depressed person. They wear emotional scars from living in a constant battleground.

Our book is designed to help other families understand the anger and the sadness of depression, and prepare them for the roller coaster ride of ups and downs they will encounter on the road to recovery. Our goal is to help them find the strength and the courage they need to work through the barriers that depression has built within their family.

As our family lived through this experience it became apparent to us that one of the most important elements in the recovery process is the love and support provided to depressed persons by their families.

As families, we need to help each other to deal with the illness of depression. Depressed family members need us even more to provide a safety net for them as they walk the high wire through a world they see as filled with pain and unhappiness.

Our book will provide some instructions on how a family coping with depression can construct a safety net. We are providing the instructions, you are the builders and, together, we can succeed in changing the old way of living into a new and more enlightened way of being.

Together, we all hold the net.

Section I

LIVING WITH THE NIGHTMARE

6

1 | The Suicide Attempt

Like most other days, October 28, 1986, began with the insistent buzz of the alarm clock. Our morning ritual of showers, breakfast, packing lunches, getting two small children ready for school was the usual fast-paced melodrama.

I had recently returned to college and I had an assignment to complete for my 9 o'clock class. I poured myself a cup of coffee and began doing my homework at the breakfast table just as my husband Dan walked into the kitchen.

"Hi, honey," I said. He didn't respond to my greeting but as he picked up his car keys he turned toward me.

"Why do you always leave the lights on in this kitchen?" he yelled in an accusatory tone. "These lights cost money, you know, and we don't have any . . . and where are the bills I need to pay?"

Caught off guard by his outburst, I scrambled for an answer. "I don't know where the bills are exactly, and I'm sorry about the lights," I said apologetically.

Feeling guilty and unnerved, I said, "I can get the bills together and give them to you tonight, if that's okay."

"Well, that's just the kind of person you are, Kellie. You're always thinking about yourself. You never give any consideration to anyone else," Dan replied as he stomped out of the house.

When I heard the door slam shut, I felt a great sense of relief. It was becoming very hard to live with someone who found fault with everything I said or did. I could never do anything to please him. I was always confused, consumed with guilt. I questioned my own actions constantly.

I really should have taken the time to look for the bills instead of continuing to work on my homework, I thought. Maybe he's right—maybe I do always think of myself.

The demons of self-doubt affect us all, especially in relationships.

By now, I could no longer concentrate on my homework assignment. I shoved it into my book bag, gathered up the two kids and we headed out the door.

Sitting in class that morning, I thought about what was happening in my relationship with Dan. We had been married for 9 years. We'd been through some rough times, but we'd tried hard to work things out. I got pregnant with our first child, Andy, almost immediately after we were married. Our relationship at that time was not solid but I attributed that to being young, poor, and newly married with a baby on the way.

The baby turned out to be the saving grace for our marriage. As a father, Dan was the best. He spent hours rocking and loving and playing with Andy. I thought that if he would just love me as much as he loved our baby, everything would be okay.

As time went on, our circumstances improved little by little. Like many young couples, we were strapped financially but we managed to buy a car and move into a nicer apartment. When I became pregnant with our second child, Dan was in heaven. He was crazy about kids and wanted a big family. He treated me like a queen throughout the pregnancy. It was the one time in our marriage that he seemed to be genuinely happy.

That happiness, however, was short-lived.

With the birth of our daughter, Susie, came the added pressures of having another mouth to feed. Both Dan and I had unrealistic ideas about the extent of the commitment needed to raise two kids. I was exhausted and discouraged. After five years of staying home taking care of kids and watching soap operas, I felt as though I had nothing to contribute anymore. Dan was overwhelmed by the awesome responsibilities he had incurred. His paycheck was spent before it arrived in the mail. We had barely enough money to survive and nothing left over for extras.

Our marriage began to suffer and we found ways of spending time away from each other. Dan began to drink excessively. I went back to school.

So, here I was sitting in class and realizing that there were many ways to leave a marriage other than getting a divorce. Dan and I had been leaving ours for a long time.

We couldn't talk to each other without getting into an argument. Dan had become distant and hard to reach. The hardest thing for me to understand was his anger—a seething, raging anger that never seemed to go away. He was angry about everything that went wrong or seemed to go wrong for him, even little things that wouldn't bother most people.

The more angry Dan became, the more he bottled it up inside himself. The bottled-up anger caused him to withdraw and isolate himself from me and the kids. The more he withdrew and isolated himself from us, the more we pulled away from him. It was a vicious cycle. We were a family trapped in a revolving door with no exits.

I thought about our situation throughout the day. Just as I had done on so many other days, I decided I just couldn't figure out what was wrong so I gave up trying and concentrated on my afternoon schedule.

After my classes were finished for the day, I went shopping for Halloween costumes for the children. Four-year-old Susie's preschool was having a Halloween party that night. Although she had been handling the day care experience well since I had returned to school, I thought it would be good for her if we all went to the party as a family.

I found perfect little Ghost and Dracula costumes, picked

9

up the kids, and we rushed home for a quick dinner. Andy and Susie were excited about going to the party and I was looking forward to us being able to spend some time together just having fun.

We were all laughing and talking and the kids were getting into their costumes when Dan came home. As he walked in I could tell from his face that his early morning anger about the bills had not dissipated during the day. He was still seething inside.

He carried a six-pack of beer into the family room and sat down to watch television. The television had become his regular dinner date and a six-pack his main course. We asked him if he wanted to go to the party with us but he ignored the invitation. I tried to ask him again and he stopped me in the middle of my sentence saying, "I'm tired, I've got a lot on my mind and I do not want to go anywhere . . . period!"

I told him I was really sorry and that we would be back in a couple of hours. I kissed him good-bye and headed out to the car with the kids.

As we pulled out of the driveway, I felt a strange sense of anxiety. It was like the fearful feeling I always got watching a lightning storm move across the valley and creep into town. I passed it off as just some momentary weird feeling because I was going to a Halloween party. Dan was always telling me I worried too much and I figured he was probably right.

When I drove out of our driveway that October evening, I was just another mom driving her children to a school activity. I didn't realize that my momentary feeling of foreboding was the signal of an approaching storm—a terrible storm that threatened to destroy four lives and left permanent scars on the souls of everyone in our family.

The kids and I arrived at the party ready for fun. Susie and Andy had a great time carving pumpkins and bobbing for apples. The teachers had done a wonderful job handling the crowds of parents with their monsters, ghosts and goblins in tow. It was fun to watch my kids enjoying themselves with the others. We seldom had fun as a family anymore.

The emotional climate we had been living in was very stressful. I never seemed able to find the time I needed to

10

spend playing and having fun with Andy and Susie. I was always on edge. I felt as if I was forever walking on egg shells trying to hold my marriage together. I worried constantly about Dan and what the next argument would bring. He demanded so much of my time and attention. I tried to fulfill his needs and to make everything okay for him. When I could not, I felt guilty. The guilt made me crazy and I felt inadequate. So, I tried even harder to please him and, still, we were living a life of constant conflict.

Watching Andy and Susie, I thought how lucky I was that they were happy, healthy and fairly well-adjusted in spite of our chaotic home life. The kids loved us both and we loved them, so why couldn't Dan and I figure out a way to love each other and make our marriage work? I wanted this so badly but I didn't know how to make it happen. I decided I would just have to love Dan more and try harder to please him so that we could all stay together.

My thoughts were interrupted by Susie winning first place in the pumpkin-carving contest!

I was upbeat and happy as we drove home. I was determined to single-handedly resolve all our marriage problems. I would help Dan feel better about himself and, if I did things his way, he would not feel so angry all the time. Somehow, everything would work out.

As I pulled into the driveway, the uneasiness I had felt earlier returned. Because I was now feeling so confident, I ignored it and helped my tiny Ghost and little Vampire out of the back seat of the car.

Dan's car was in the garage but the house was unusually dark and all the blinds on the windows were closed. As we walked in the door, I called to Dan but there was no response.

The kids followed me as I hurried down the narrow hallway that led to the master bedroom. The door was closed. As I turned the knob, I heard a sob. My sense of uneasiness turned into panic. I opened the door quickly. The room was black.

I flipped on the light and realized the crying sounds were coming from the walk-in closet. I opened the door to the closet and found my husband sitting on the floor with a gun to his head.

For a silent moment, we were held motionless as in a

freeze-frame of a video tape. My first thought was, "This is not really happening and if I close my eyes it will all go away."

I think Dan was as shocked to see me and the children standing in the doorway as we were to see him with the gun. The silence was broken by seven-year-old Andy's scream. It was so compelling that Dan immediately dropped the gun. I think, for a split second, he thought about the lives he was about to destroy. If he killed himself, he would also kill a part of me and his children as well.

He let the gun fall to the floor of the closet and began to sob again. The reality of what was happening had begun to sink in and I realized that we were trapped in a terrible nightmare and that we could all end up dead if I didn't find a way out fast.

I was so afraid and felt so overwhelmed that I started to cry. Then, I looked at my children, still in their costumes, frantic, terrified, and begging me to help their dad.

Andy, with tears running down the white paint on his Dracula face was screaming, "Please, Dad, don't shoot it. Mom, do something!!"

I said what was true. "I want to help him. I just don't know what to do anymore."

Dan continued to sob uncontrollably. I tried to touch him, to comfort and hold him but he screamed at me to leave him alone. "You all just use me. I don't need you. All you do is cost me money," he screamed.

I knew I had to get the kids out of there. The gun was still within Dan's reach and I was afraid he might grab it and shoot them or me or himself in front of them. I told them to go out and sit in the hall. They did not want to leave but I gave them a look that was so pleading they did what I asked.

Now, there was more room in the closet. I tried to collect my thoughts and figure out the best way to handle the situation. My emotions were running wild but I was trying to be extremely careful about what I said and how I said it. For what seemed like an eternity, I said nothing but just listened to Dan sob and sob.

Thousands of thoughts were running through my mind. "What should I do? What should I say?" Here was a man who was totally shattered and was literally falling apart in front of me. I had never been around anyone who had ever gone through anything like this and I felt lost.

Then, like a dark cloud, the guilt hit me. It was all my fault. If I had done this or that better . . . if I had been there for him . . . if I were more understanding . . . none of this would have happened. It was all my fault and now I didn't know what to do.

In that brief moment, I took on Dan's suicide attempt as my responsibility. It seemed clear to me that this was not only a suicide attempt, but a way for Dan to escape the marriage and the emotional hell we had been living in for the past several years. And I had created the hell! He was right. I was responsible for his behavior.

I had to get the gun away from him. He was still huddled in the back of the closet. Silently, I slid the gun across the carpet on the closet floor. All of a sudden, he jumped up and started yelling at me. He screamed through his tears that he hated me, hated our life together, that I had ruined his life. He lunged towards the phone in our bedroom and I panicked.

I could not imagine who he would want to call in the frame of mind he was in but I stood still. I heard him ask directory assistance for a local crisis/hotline number. He did it in such a matter-of-fact way, as if he had thought about calling them many times before. I waited silently in the closet as he dialed the number. I heard him tell the crisis counselor on the other end of the line that he had just tried to kill himself but that his family had walked in on him and now he didn't know what to do.

He seemed to become totally involved in the telephone conversation and unaware of what was going on around him in the house. Without letting him see what I was doing, I managed to slide the gun out of the closet, across the bedroom floor and past my two children who were still sitting terrified in the hall. I tried to communicate to them with my eyes that they needed to hang on for a few more minutes. They seemed to read my mind and they did not move.

I carried the gun out of the house and put it under a shelf in the garage and covered it with a sleeping bag. I did not want to take the chance of Dan finding it again. I hurried back into the house. The kids were where I had left them and I could hear Dan crying and talking on the phone. I felt an enormous sense of relief to know that at last someone else was carrying some of the burden and keeping him on the phone so that I could think for a minute about what to do with the kids.

I gathered them up and took them into the bathroom. We sat on the floor and I told them that something was really wrong with their dad (as if they hadn't figured that out by now) and that we were all going to have to hang together until we got this worked out. I washed off their make-up and got them out of their costumes and ready for bed. I had no idea where they or any of us would sleep that night or any night in the near future but just going through the normal routine motions was comforting to all of us.

Dan was on the phone for almost two hours and when he finally hung up, he was exhausted physically and mentally. The hotline people had given him the telephone number of a therapist in town they thought he should see and he agreed to do that. He walked over to the bed, lay down on it and immediately went to sleep. The crisis was over for now but I decided that whatever happened, I would figure out a way to get us all some help to end the nightmare we were living.

2 | Getting Help: No Place To Hide

After Dan's suicide attempt, I felt desperate. I had no idea where to turn or whom to ask for help. I was not working at the time and had no money of my own to pay for counseling. Even if I'd had unlimited resources, the idea of trying to talk to someone, especially someone I did not even know, about all of our personal problems seemed unthinkable.

I really believed that everything was my fault. I felt so much guilt about what had happened that, to me, talking to a marriage counselor would have been like confessing my sins to the entire Catholic Church.

How could I trust anyone with such a terrible secret? How could anyone sit and listen to all of it and not think I was a witch to live with? What if someone found out I was going to a therapist?

I had so many fears about counseling that it seemed easier to ignore them than to seek help and find some solutions.

Dan, on the other hand, had already called the therapist recommended by the crisis line counselor. We waited three days for him to call back with an appointment time. During those three days, we both did a lot of thinking. Dan spent his time thinking about how I had ruined his life, and I spent my time feeling guilty and afraid of what was going to happen when he went to his first appointment with this unknown family therapist.

I had very mixed emotions about the whole thing. I was glad that Dan was willing to get some counseling because I knew we could not live in a constant state of conflict anymore. But I also knew that once he opened up and started to talk, he would blame me for all the despair he had been feeling. I had stood by him throughout our 9 years together but, during the months preceding the suicide attempt, I knew I hadn't given 100 percent of my love and devotion to our marriage. It had become extremely difficult for me to support and love this man who verbally ripped me to shreds at every opportunity for no apparent reason.

Up until now, Dan's verbal abuse and constant reminding me of all my faults was always done in the privacy of our own home. Now he was going to tell some stranger about all the things I had done to push him over the edge. That was hard for me to swallow. I wanted to support his plan of going for help and yet I did not want him to go in and tell all our family secrets. I thought that, on Dan's word, I would be judged and found guilty by an unknown therapist without ever having a chance to defend myself.

I had to dig down deep in my inner soul to find the strength to be supportive of the counseling. I thought maybe, just maybe, the therapist would understand the hell I had been living in and would know that I was not really the terrible person my husband said I was.

When the day of his appointment came, Dan was very angry. He would not tell me where he was going or who he was seeing. I only knew about the appointment because I had overheard part of his telephone conversation with the therapist.

When he left the house to go to the therapist's office, a

part of me wished he would never come back. I was relieved that he was gone. It gave me a chance to reflect on what we had been going through and I realized that our lives were entangled in chains—chains that we could not break by ourselves.

A part of me hoped the therapist would tell him the marriage was hopeless and there was no way we could work things out. At least that way we would both feel "off the hook" and not responsible for a divorce. Neither one of us really believed in divorce but if someone told us there was no way we could ever work things out, we would have an instant escape route through a divorce court rather than having to face working through all the problems we shared. Even if a divorce ultimately turned out to be the wrong answer, we could blame the therapist for the decision, not ourselves or each other.

When he came home from his first session, he would not tell me anything about the person he was seeing but he did say he had another appointment in a couple of days. To me, that meant that he had found the session productive enough to spend the money to go back again. I assumed he must have somehow "connected" with the therapist he was seeing.

This was a big step because money was one of the most important things in Dan's life. He would never waste a dime. The idea that he was going to pay someone for therapy, which he had always said he didn't believe in anyway, meant that something good had happened in that first session.

Because he seemed so eager to go back, I really wanted to know what had happened while he was there. I asked him how it went. He said he had told "the guy" about "all the crap you have been doing to me and how much you cost me all the time and about how much you use me."

I felt as if I had been slapped. Although I had expected him to say all those things, I had secretly hoped I might be wrong.

Dan said that "the guy" really understood what it was like to have to live with someone who was such a bitch and agreed that Dan had every right to be angry as hell at the way things were going in his life.

It was apparent to me that Dan really believed this "guy" was on his side and was behind him all the way. That worried me. I couldn't imagine that anyone would or could be on his side. What I didn't know at the time was that the therapist was beginning the process of establishing a therapeutic alliance with Dan, an alliance that required a great deal of trust.

When Dan went into that office for his first therapy session, he did not trust anyone. He met someone there who let him feel that he was supported no matter what. Dan had become the star of his own therapy session and no one else was more important. I think, for the first time in his life, he experienced a sense of unconditional regard. No matter what he said or did the therapist understood how he felt. In Dan's mind, they had become allies. In my mind, there was total confusion.

Dan did mention, in passing that evening, one other thing. "The guy thinks I'm depressed. He wants me to go to some doctor for some pills."

Depressed? Pills? I could have told the therapist a million things that I thought were wrong with Dan but "depressed" would not have been any one of them. How can he be depressed, I thought, when he acts like such a jerk all the time?

In my mind, Dan certainly had no reason to be depressed. He had everything listed in the Great American Dream catalog —a nice wife, a couple of beautiful healthy children, a home of his own, and he had recently opened his own business. He had just turned 32 and was doing pretty well for himself.

If anyone should have felt depressed, it should have been me. I was the one who had to live with his anger and his put-downs every day. To me, being depressed was just having a bad day or a bad week when everything went wrong and I felt down in the dumps and miserable. I was sure no one ever stayed like that for a long time.

Whenever I felt "depressed" I'd mope around for a while, watch an old movie, cry my eyes out and then pull myself out of it. Or I'd get busy working on a project to stimulate my mind, go visit friends, or get involved in some other kind of activity. Within a few hours my mood would pick up and life would feel okay again.

I didn't know the therapist Dan was seeing but I felt I really needed to talk to "this guy." Somehow, he had his diagnosis all wrong. There was no way that depression was the problem in our marriage.

After Dan went to bed that night, I searched the desk and in the back of the phone book I found the name "Dale Babcock" and a telephone number scratched into the cover. The next morning, after Dan left for work, I called Dale.

I was filled with apprehension as I dialed the number. I didn't know anything about this Dale Babcock and I was sure he knew everything bad that could ever be said about me. Luckily, he was not in his office when I called and his answering service said he would have to call me back. That was good because it gave me time to plot my strategy for telling him what was really happening between Dan and me.

When Dale called that evening I was prepared to unload all my pain. I told him that I was very concerned about this "depression" diagnosis and that I didn't think he was right about it. He was accepting of the fact that I could not see depression in Dan but assured me it was there. He told me that this type of depression was not just a case of the "blues" or a bad case of burnout.

He asked me some questions. Had I noticed that Dan had no appetite? Hadn't been sleeping? Been extremely irritated at little things? Had difficulty concentrating? Had trouble remembering things? He asked when was the last time I had seen Dan read a book? If he had been drinking a lot? Had he lost his drive for sex?

To most of these, I answered a bewildered "yes."

Dale than explained that these were classic symptoms of something called a "major depressive episode" and that Dan needed to get on some medication to help him feel better. When he felt better, Dale assured me, he would act better.

Dale then asked me to come to Dan's next appointment and, in the meantime, encourage him to see the psychiatrist he had recommended for a medical evaluation and some medication. Somewhat reluctantly I agreed to his recommendations and thanked him for his time. As I hung up the phone, I realized two new words had entered my vocabulary—"depression" and "psychiatrist."

The latter was a word that I had never used and barely heard. Now, my husband was going to meet with one of them. My casual spark of interest in the subject of depression was beginning to flame. I wanted to find out more.

3 | Depression: What Is It?

Depression is the most common mental illness in the world today. It affects all age groups and social/economic groups. In some cases it is barely noticeable and in others, totally disabling. The National Institute of Mental Health estimates that approximately 20 million Americans will suffer from some kind of depressive illness this year.

After talking with Dale, I searched the shelves of the local library for clues in the mystery of depression. I came across several books written by people who had suffered from this illness. As I read their descriptions of their experiences, I began to understand the extent of their pain. One woman said it all, "You don't have to die to go to hell, you just have to be depressed."

In his book, *The Good News About Depression,* Dr. Dan Gold talks about the history of depression. The Greeks thought that personality was determined by the fluids in the body. Those who had a predominance of black bile were determined to be melancholic.

In the middle ages, depression was treated as a problem with the person's spirit. The depressed person was thought to be possessed by evil and demonic spirits.

Some of our greatest writers and political leaders have been affected by it. Shakespeare projected his depression into his work. Abraham Lincoln told of his depression in a letter he sent to his law partner John Stewart:

"I am now the most miserable man living. If what I feel were equally distributed to the whole human family, there would not be one cheerful face on the earth. Whether I shall be better I cannot tell; I awfully forbode I shall not. To remain as I am is impossible. I must die or be better . . . ."

Winston Churchill referred to his depression as "the black dog." Senator Thomas Eagleton's publicized treatment for depression had a substantial negative impact on his political career.

Today, more than ever before, more and more people are willing to speak publicly about the illness. Author William Styron, actor John Cleese, and Kitty Dukakis, wife of former Massachusetts Governor Michael Dukakis, all have written books about their experiences with the dark clouds of depression. Mike Wallace, Rod Steiger, Larry King, Betty Ford, Tai Babilonia and many other celebrities are speaking about their experiences with the illness and their own treatment process.

As I continued to read, I learned that depression is an illness that involves both the mind and the body. It is characterized by unpleasant moods, feelings of hopelessness and sadness, and a loss of energy.

While not all depressed persons consider suicide, I was frightened to discover that depression is a major contributing factor to the alarming rise in the numbers of deaths by suicide in this country.

NOT JUST ANOTHER CASE OF THE BLUES

All of us experience depression at one time or another. It's a normal part of everyday living. It's natural for anyone to feel down in the dumps and sad from time to time.

Normal depression can be brought on by any unhappiness or loss that we feel. A business or personal failure, a change of seasons, or stressful holidays also can trigger feelings of depression. Grief is a major component of normal depression. The intense grief brought on by the death of a family member or a close friend or even a beloved pet is normal and usually eases with the passage of time. Even though the memories remain clear and vivid, the pain seems to fade as the days and years go by and most people eventually get on with their lives.

Normal depression is natural and provides us with an opportunity to recognize and identify the incredible power we have within ourselves to overcome adversity and to create new visions for our future.

How do we know the difference between "normal" depression and serious or clinical depression?

Individuals who are "clinically depressed" feel as if they have no inner strength to tap into. Unlike people who suffer from normal depression and eventually recover, clinically depressed people are not able to get on with their lives. They become almost paralyzed mentally for weeks, months and sometimes even years.

They feel totally drained, completely exhausted and have no hope for the future. They see the world as a black hole through a distorted window in their mind. Often, they seem to have no will to live. Clinical depression is a complex illness that can vary in degree from mild to severe.

WHAT DEPRESSION FEELS LIKE

As I continued my reading about people who had experienced this kind of depression, I found that when they described it, they said things like:

"a feeling of worthlessness and hopelessness . . ."

"an overwhelming sadness . . . that I just cannot shake."

23

"It feels like being trapped in a dark closet and not being able to find a way out."

"I feel really ugly on the inside, I hate who I am and I hate how I act, but I can't change. I don't have any control over myself anymore."

"I felt sad and guilty all the time."

"I just want to die so I don't have to be a burden on anyone anymore."

Some depressed people experience symptoms so severe that they literally cannot function. They may not be able to get out of bed in the morning or get to sleep at night. They may lose their appetite or eat compulsively causing them to lose or gain weight. Family members may notice the depressed person suffering physically from more headaches, digestive disorders, and chronic aches and pains. Some people get agitated and act nervous, while others become very slow-moving and slow-reacting.

Seriously depressed people find no joy in any of the activities they once found pleasurable. They show little if any interest in sex, although a small percentage of them may have a heightened desire for sex. Usually, they are tired all the time. They feel worthless. They may feel guilty and afraid of seemingly trivial things. They find it difficult to concentrate on a task—reading the newspaper is a real challenge. They may have trouble making decisions and when they finally do make a decision, they can't remember what it was or why they made it. They may be very irritable, exhibit a lack of patience and get very angry over minor things.

Sadness is a constant symptom of depression. Those suffering from it often break into tears for no apparent reason. Chronic sadness, coupled with the feelings of hopelessness and helplessness lead the depressed person to believe there is no hope—no way out.

As the depression drags on, the symptoms become more intense. The depressed person's relationships with family members and close friends deteriorate. Their ability to communicate diminishes over a period of months or years. They may withdraw from friends and others and become silent and angry. Because men seem to find anger easier to express, they may display their irritability and rage while women tend to hold their anger inside. Either way, the anger is destructive to family relationships.

Depressed persons see no good in the world or in anyone who lives in it. They focus on unhappy events and the failures in their lives. Almost everything they say is negative. It does not matter what anyone says to "try to perk them up." Nothing works.

Some depressed people have recurring thoughts of suicide. They often say they just want to feel numb. They want the pain to go away but they don't know how to get rid of it so they think they should get rid of themselves. Death seems to be the only way out for them.

DIFFERENT KINDS OF DEPRESSION

Doctors, therapists, and psychologists use different terms to describe depression—Clinical Depression, Manic, Dysthymia, Biological, and Melancholic, just to name a few. It helps to understand these terms and to recognize the various forms depression takes.

Clinical depression means that the symptoms are severe and long-lasting and will require some form of treatment.

Major depression indicates that a clinical depression has been further investigated usually by a doctor or a psychiatrist and has been found to meet specific diagnostic criteria established in the mental health community. Depression at this level usually has been going on for a long time and probably has affected the person's functioning in physical, emotional and intellectual ways. Major is the most common type of depression.

Bi-polar or Manic-depression is a form of depression with severe mood swings, alternating between extreme lows and manic highs. People who suffer from Manic-depression are on a constant roller coaster of ups and downs—manic on the ups and depressed on the downs. In a manic state, these people show inappropriate elation, have "big idea thinking" and feel invincible. Racing thoughts, fast talking and moving and increased sexual activity characterize this type of depression.

Manic-depressives have too much energy—they can stay up all night for days at a time. Their thinking is irrational and they sometimes attempt the impossible or dangerous with no regard for the consequences of their behavior. When they are happy and gregarious, they can be fun to be around. They like to go on extravagant vacations or extensive shopping sprees that empty their bank accounts and run up their credit cards to the limit. If confronted about their irrational behavior, they become hostile and defensive.

In time, however, the manic phase ends and the roller coaster ride starts down towards its inevitable crash. The mood then becomes just as low as it was high. These people show all the classic symptoms of depression with one major difference—in extreme cases, they may become delusional. They may start to hallucinate. They may see suicide as the only way out of their depression and they will attempt it unless they begin receiving treatment.

Dysthymia is a term used for long-term mild depression. It is a type of depression that can be temporarily altered but never really goes away. It is not totally disabling but can keep the depressed person from reaching his or her full potential.

Bio-chemical or Biological depression describes a connection between the depression, the chemistry of the brain and the workings of the body.

Melancholic is a term used to describe a severe major depression.

Depression is often present with other disabling disorders such as anorexia, anxiety-related health problems and obsessive-compulsive disorders. It may manifest itself by shaking, sweating, or shortness of breath.

HOW COULD THIS HAPPEN TO US?

Depression can attack any one of us at any time. It can start in childhood and go unrecognized for years. Most experts now feel that there are three sets of factors—psychological, biological and interpersonal—that contribute to the onset of depression.

Psychological Factors: The most common contributors to an individual's depression are psychological factors that have altered his or her life. Personality traits influence the vulnerability to depression. People who have persistent negative thought patterns, are constantly critical of the people around them, their jobs and their lives, are putting themselves within striking range of depression.

People who become consumed with guilt over insignificant faults, or who focus on how hopeless their lives are, eventually become overwhelmed with stress and prone to depression. Unrealistic expectations and low self-esteem contribute to the illness. The mind begins to believe what the thoughts are saying.

People who are depressed truly believe that they are failures and view life as a terrible experience. Continually viewing the world from this perspective causes a person to become psychologically disabled and unable to change his perceptions without help.

Biological Factors: A person may have an illness that disrupts the normal functioning of the body and, thus, causes depression. Some medications interact with the body in such a way as to cause a depression reaction.

Researchers studying the brain now believe that depression can be a biological problem. Much like a diabetic whose body refuses to produce insulin and proceeds to get out of balance, the depressed person's brain chemistry can become altered and out of balance.

The brain is composed of a network of nerve endings that are separated from each other by gaps known as synapses. Messages are sent via chemical-electrical reactions across the synapse by a variety of neurotransmitters resulting in thoughts and feelings. The brain keeps the balance of neurotransmitters at a normal level. Depression results when this delicate balance somehow becomes altered. The right anti-depressant medication seems to return the chemistry to normal levels.

Researchers also are currently looking at substantial evidence that seems to establish the fact that depression may run in families. Depression rates are much higher among children of depressed parents than among the general population. As hard as these people try to resist it, sometimes the depression just overwhelms them. Personal strength, it seems, cannot always overcome genetics.

When one family member is depressed, it's a good idea to check the family tree for cousins, uncles, grandparents, aunts, or anyone in the preceding two or three generations who may have suffered from some kind of mental illness, emotional breakdown or from a potentially unrecognized depression, such as alcoholism or substance abuse.

Research in this area is progressing at a fast pace. Perhaps within the next 10 years depression will be declared as an inherited illness. This would be a major breakthrough because it would help some people to understand that their depression is not their "fault" and there may be a biological problem that is causing it. Understanding that may be enough to alleviate the stigma attached to depression and enable more people to seek treatment and begin to heal themselves and improve their lives.

Interpersonal Factors: When depressed people are asked why they are depressed, the first answer usually is something like, "Well, my husband says he doesn't love me anymore," or "I just can't put my finger on why I am depressed, although I didn't get the promotion I really wanted at work."

These statements are reflections of the interpersonal (sometimes referred to as environmental) factors that influence depression. Shattered dreams and broken relationships play a big role in one's state of mind. Disappointments, business failures, a divorce or an illness can begin the downward spiral of depression.

Transitions can bring on depression. Transitions in relationships, parenthood, or simply in the roles of the family members can be devastating to the person susceptible to depression.

Life sometimes presents us with problems and tragedies that we are not prepared to deal with. These traumatic events can tax the mental and emotional capacities of an individual to the limit and may result in depression.

Counselors often see another factor of interpersonal

depression when someone comes into the office for therapy. They say people have "interpersonal deficits" when they lack the communication skills or the knowledge to enable them to relate well with other people. This inability to relate causes havoc in their lives. They can't keep a job. They bounce from marriage to marriage and can't figure out why. They wonder what it is about them that causes so much disruption in their lives and in the lives of the people around them.

Unresolved conflicts can lead to depression. Harsh religious backgrounds with many shoulds and should nots can be a factor. High achievers are more subject to depression. Workaholism often is a mask for depression.

By the time I had finished looking through books and magazine articles about this illness, I knew that going into therapy was truly our last hope to beat the depression and save our family. It was scary to think about going to a therapist but, after all my reading, it was more scary not to go. The dark clouds were beginning to clear. I thought perhaps we could live through the storm.

4 | In Search of Ourselves

THE FIRST APPOINTMENT TOGETHER

Driving to my first therapy appointment was a really scary experience. My mind was a jumble of confused thoughts. I had no idea what to expect and Dan had told me very little about what his first session had been like. Anxiety and fear were my companions.

We had driven separate cars and Dan was waiting when I walked in. It seemed so strange to be sitting there waiting to see a therapist. We didn't talk to each other. We sat and stared at the wall. There were other people in the room and I wondered what kind of people they were and why they were there.

We sat in the waiting room for only about ten minutes but it seemed like ten hours. Finally, Dale walked out and said "hello" to Dan. I thought to myself, there is no way this could be "the guy." I had it in my mind that a therapist should look

31

like a judge and be very quiet and aloof. Standing in front of me introducing himself was a warm and friendly person dressed in casual clothes who seemed open and sympathetic. He talked to us for a few minutes and then asked me if I would like a cola.

I thought it was really odd. I felt as if I was a guest at someone's house but a cold drink sounded good so I told him I'd like one and he handed it to me as he led us down the hall to his office.

With a cold cola in my hand and a warm feeling inside, I was beginning to feel more relaxed with "the guy" and with the whole idea of trying out therapy.

Dale's office was comfortable. We sat down and I noticed his desk was positioned against the wall. There was nothing between the three of us except space. I liked that. It felt good to me.

We spent the hour answering questions about our relationship and Dan's depression. We talked a little about our pasts and we began to plan for the following week. Dan had agreed to see a psychiatrist and he was waiting to get an appointment. He was still very depressed and we needed to come up with some ways to get through the next few days. I was worried about him attempting suicide again and Dale helped us to formulate some strategies to deal with that problem.

At the end of the hour, Dale told us it was time to stop for now but he would like to see us at the end of the week after Dan had seen the psychiatrist. We wrote him a check for the session, thanked him and left.

I felt better. Dan and I hadn't solved anything yet but we had been given a little gift that would carry us through the next three years of therapy. That gift was hope. Dale had helped us to define what was happening in our lives and he encouraged us to look at some options and make some choices about how we wanted things to be in the future. Knowing there was someone else who cared about us and about saving our tattered marriage helped me feel more secure and more stable in the relationship.

FINDING A THERAPIST

Dan and I were extremely fortunate to find a competent and understanding therapist in a world of many choices from among the mental health professions. It had never occurred to me before that either one of us might need counseling at some point in our lives. I had never been around anyone (that I knew of) who suffered from mental illness. I had no idea whom to call for help.

When Dan called the crisis line in our city, I realized that was a resource I had never thought of. Crisis lines are staffed with volunteers who are trained in crisis intervention. They have access to a bank of therapists and usually will be able to connect a caller with someone who specializes in the problems associated with depression.

Choosing a therapist is a challenging task. It should be done with a great deal of care and thought. There are many different kinds of therapists using both conventional and unconventional methods of treatment.

From the conventional side, there are licensed counselors, social workers, psychologists, psychiatrists, and medical doctors. In addition, many people seek help from their religious leaders. Pastors, priests, bishops and others are often consulted for advice and family counseling.

There are almost as many different types of therapy as there are people in the world. Everyone is different and what works for some people may not work for others.

To my mind, the absolute best way to find a good therapist is to get a referral. Getting advice from friends or family who have been in therapy can be invaluable. It gives you a perspective about a therapist that is hard to come by without actually knowing that person yourself. You can get an idea about the type of therapy he or she does, whom they have helped and how effectively they have empowered people to improve their lives, etc.

It is important to remember, that the perspective you get is just that, a perspective. It is one person's opinion. One person may really connect with a therapist and another person may not. Usually, if someone has had a good experience with a therapist, he/she is willing to share that information much more readily than is someone who has had a bad experience.

There is one problem with word-of-mouth referrals, however. It is rare that anyone actually shares information about a family member's depressive illness or attempted suicide. Rarely do any of us ever bring up the subject of or ask about any treatment that someone has received for mental illness.

Most of us think nothing of asking our friends for the name of a good doctor in town, but very few of us feel comfortable inquiring about a good therapist or marriage counselor.

Other avenues to pursue in finding help include obtaining referrals from local hospitals, mental health organizations, and non-profit agencies such as battered women's shelters and rape crisis programs.

Another important resource is the family doctor. In the new age of family medicine, more and more physicians are becoming aware that a patient's physical state is highly influenced by his mental and emotional state. They are aware of the stress and anxiety-related problems we all face in our struggle to keep up with the fast pace of today's world. The family doctor may be the one individual in whom a depressed person and his family feel comfortable about confiding their family secrets. The family doctor also can provide help and/or referral information that the depressed person can trust and feel good about pursuing.

A DIFFERENT KIND OF HELP

Depression like any other chronic illness has its share of unconventional healers. These include people like massage therapists, metaphysical healers who scan the body looking for blockages and energy imbalances, and psychics who claim to have answers to what is causing the depression. Attitudenal healers work on the unconscious mind by creating affirmations and visualizations that are uplifting and spiritually enlightening. All of these methods may work for some people.

The only proven method that works in dealing with depression, from the point of view of the scientific and medical community, is a combination of cognitive therapy, drug therapy and interpersonal therapy. Cognitive therapy is usually practiced only by those in the mental health professions such as counselors, social workers, psychologists and psychiatrists.

Just because it is a proven technique does not mean that it stands alone in the fight against depression. As we all realize, science does not have all the answers to everything. We still know very little about the mind and how it works. If visualizing peaceful scenes makes a depressed person feel less depressed, it may be worthwhile for that person to pursue a more unconventional way of treatment.

In my opinion, the last resort in picking a therapist would be sorting through the telephone book or newspaper advertising. The yellow pages are a great place to advertise but choosing a therapist from them is like buying a lottery ticket. It's simply a game of chance, picking a name and number and hoping that it might prove to be the winning ticket. Those are pretty high odds against which to play your own or your loved one's emotional health.

Regardless of how one goes about finding a therapist, that therapist should be someone who really cares about the depressed person and the family, someone who is supportive and who provides real understanding. A therapist should be there for his or her clients in times of crisis. Clients are taking a risk when they share their innermost thoughts and feelings and they need to have someone they can trust implicitly.

COULD I PLEASE BE EXCUSED FROM THIS WILDERNESS?

Once you have chosen a therapist, you really don't know if you have connected with the right person until you meet for the first time.

During that first session, there is usually a lot of apprehension and nervous tension on the part of the client. One of the therapist's responsibilities is to help him or her relax.

Many clinicians ask family members and significant others to attend therapy sessions with the depressed person so they can gain an understanding of what depression is and how to cope with it.

Therapy tends to be a time of great sharing. If family members are involved in the sharing of the problems, they can be more supportive of the depressed person's efforts to get well. Because of the intense emotional connections that are made, there is a sense of bonding that occurs during therapy.

When families go to the first therapy session together, they are asked to answer many questions relating to the family history and the current family status. What changes have occurred in the family during the last year? Was there a move? Was there a change of job? Any sickness? Any significant losses, such as deaths in the family, etc.?

Most likely, at some point during the session, the therapist will ask what the clients want to work on in therapy. Not knowing the answer to that question is perfectly normal. Many people who feel bad can't figure out what their problems are, much less which ones they need to work on the most. A major part of therapy is sorting through all the difficulties of the depressed person's life and then deciding which ones to tackle. Clients should just say what they feel. There are no wrong answers in therapy.

Therapists ask questions to gather information. They are, in effect, creating a frame for future therapy. The depressed person's life is like a 1500-piece jigsaw puzzle with all the pieces jumbled together in the box and no clues as to how they fit together.

The therapist takes the client's answers to his questions and begins to build a frame that helps him to guide the depressed person and the family through a process of looking at each piece of the puzzle of their lives and deciding how it all fits together. In this way, the therapist can begin to clarify confusing issues and pinpoint trouble areas that need to be addressed.

A major advantage of the therapeutic process is that it allows another person (the therapist) to enter a depressed person's world and reality as that person sees it. The therapist can then take an objective look at what pieces of the puzzle are missing and help the depressed person figure out how to find them or replace them.

Many people believe that the only ones who go to a therapist are crazy and neurotic people and that the therapist spends the hour analyzing every word they say. While that may be true in some cases, most of the time people who seek treatment or try to get help with depression, or any other problems, are ordinary people just like you or your next door neighbor or the person who sits at the desk next to you in the office, people who are tired of trying to handle everything alone. Because of that mistaken belief about therapy, it is not uncommon near the end of the first session for someone to ask, "Am I going crazy?" or "How messed up am I really, compared to other people you see?"

Most therapists will respond by smiling and saying, "You're not going crazy, even though you may feel like it at times. The truth is that you are quite normal and that you need some help getting through the pain you are feeling."

So, in addition to finding out they are not crazy, by the end of the first therapy hour, clients have some idea of what is happening in their lives and they should have some good feelings about their therapist.

GETTING THE MOST OUT OF THERAPY

For depressed persons and their loved ones who are going into therapy, there are some simple strategies that help to give the therapeutic process the best chance of working out successfully. These include the following:

1. Be on time for appointments. It helps the therapist keep to his schedule so that clients, including yourself, will not have to be kept waiting. If you find that you can't make it to the session at the appointed time, call and re-schedule your appointment.

2. Go to the therapy session prepared to work. Good therapy is hard work. It takes a lot of mental concentration and effort. If your mind is not focused on what you are supposed to be working on, the session will not be very

37

productive. Also, try not to go into therapy exhausted. When you are tired you don't think as clearly as you would normally. It's difficult to do mental and emotional work with a sleepy mind. Remember, most sessions only last an hour, and the sooner you start working the more work you'll get done.

3. Go to the therapy session prepared to risk. Risking is one of the keys to growth in the process of healing. It's like learning to ice skate. If you aren't falling down, you aren't learning. Taking the risk to glide on those blades is a tough choice. Taking the risk to find out your own "truths" is an even tougher one. Risking means progress and progress means moving towards a better life. Just as in skating, once you start gliding forward, taking a risk becomes much easier.

4. Be honest. This is one of the most important rules of therapy. If you are honest with yourself and with your pain, it is easier to work through it and deal with it. If you are continually twisting the truth, therapy can become a tangled web that will be hard to work your way out of. This creates a situation that can be frustrating for both you and your therapist.

5. Be willing to do some homework. Most therapists will have some kind of work for you to do before the next session. They have asked you to do it because they have seen how well it has worked for other clients in the past and they believe it will help you in your healing process. This homework can take many forms. It can be written work, such as journal writing or letter writing. It can be physical work, like taking a walk every night or exercising three times a week. Or it could also be mental work, like keeping track of dreams, recalling the past or visualizing the hopes you have for the future. Whatever the work is, if you agree to do it, do it. Like chicken soup, it will make you feel better.

COMMITTING TO SUCCEED

One thing should be very clear—if you want good results from your therapy, you must be willing to make a commitment to succeed. This is very important because until you really commit to working through your problems, you will remain stuck in them. If you decide you want to make significant changes in your life, you need to make a commitment to do everything in your power to create an appropriate situation for making those changes.

Committing to succeed means doing it all—working hard in your therapy sessions and practicing what you have learned in your daily life between appointments. It means going against the odds and risking "what is" for "all that could be" in your life. It means accepting the fact that your family relationships have suffered from the depression and that it is time to heal the wounds and get on with your lives.

It also means a financial commitment. You are going to hire a consultant to evaluate your life and help you find more effective ways to deal with your problems. You may have to give up some material things of life while you invest money in healing your relationships and securing your future. The power you will gain to change the dysfunctional patterns of your family life is a direct reflection of the strength of your commitment to make that change.

Commitment is essential to progress. You may have hired the best marriage counselor who is diligently working to save your marriage and family. If you don't want to commit to that marriage and the therapy, however, there is no way it will ever work. It takes a conscious effort by everyone involved.

5 | M&M's – Medications and Medical Doctors/ Hospitals

After our first therapy session, Dan and I continued our search for help. We both somewhat understood why a medical evaluation was so important. We were literally hungry for a diagnosis. Dale had explained the illness to us and told us why medical intervention was a necessary part of the process.

We learned that severe depression is and always has been a complex and hard-to-treat illness. While psychotherapy is valuable in treating many aspects of the disease, experts now believe that medications may be a substantial part of the treatment process.

A CHEMICAL ARRANGEMENT

Extensive research now seems to indicate that depression results when certain cells in the brain receive too little of two vital chemicals, the neurotransmitters norepinephrine and seratonin. One of the purposes of medication is to make more of these chemicals available to nerve cells in the brain.

In normal people, the brain regulates the chemical flow by a process called "re-uptake." Depressed people, however, apparently need more chemicals than their brains allow them to produce. Medications that block the "re-uptake" process allow more of the chemicals to become available to the nerve cells to work against the depression.

Current research is leaning more and more towards a bio-chemical definition of depression and towards using a combination of psychological and medical treatment in its cure.

LOOKING FOR CLUES

There are a number of medical problems that can cause depression including:

– Glandular problems such as dysfunctions of the thyroid, adrenal, or pituitary glands.

– Infections and certain tumors.

– Lupus and other auto-immune diseases.

– Mononucleosis, Hepatitis and other viral infections. These may lead to depression even after the physical symptoms have disappeared and the person seems to be getting well.

– Cancer. Some tumors release chemicals that travel into the brain to cause imbalances that disrupt brain activity. This occurs mainly in cancer of the lung, pancreas and kidneys.

– Minor or major head injuries. Even a minor head injury with a short period of unconsciousness can trigger a depression weeks or months later.

In addition to these potential medical causes of depression, hormonal imbalances can also trigger depression.

Also, there are several drugs people take for other illnesses that can produce depression as a side effect. Among these are hypertension medications, steroids, birth control pills and gastrointestinal medications. If a person has a family history of the disease or has suffered with previous episodes of depression his chances of experiencing side effects of depression from these drugs increases dramatically.

For the most part, depression resulting from medical

problems can be handled by treating the illness involved or by changing the medication which is causing the depression.

GETTING SOME HELP

Medical treatment for depression is a complicated process. There are several kinds of treatment available.

The first place most people start is with their family doctor. A family doctor already knows the patient and is someone with whom the depressed person usually feels comfortable.

A family doctor will assess the overall signs and symptoms, do a routine physical exam and take a family history. Most family physicians are well aware of the manifestation of depression. They will usually prescribe medications, see how the patient feels after a couple of weeks, and then adjust the level or type of medication if necessary. This two to three-week waiting period is extremely hard on families, particularly those who expect a "magic pill" to "cure" the depression right away.

Treating depression with medication has been a standard course for many doctors but state-of-the-art testing procedures now are beginning to define depression in a biological context which is leading to a new technology in diagnosis and treatment. Many doctors now use specific blood tests to determine imbalances or other problems that may be causing the depression.

Other professionals a depressed person may want to see include internists, psychiatrists or biopsychiatrists. Each of these specialists can provide an individual specialty approach to the treatment of depression.

Women who get depressed tend to seek out the opinion of their gynecologist. This may be due in part to the fact that the ob/gyn is the one doctor a woman sees regularly. The ob/gyn is usually knowledgeable about depression and will check for hormonal imbalances and other problems that may cause depression in some women.

If a glandular or auto-immune problem is suspected it might be wise to consult with an internist who understands these problems and their contribution to depression. The internist can chart a course of action based on the particular illness.

Psychiatrists and biopsychiatrists are medical doctors with additional training in their specialized field. Like any doctor, they can prescribe medications. They usually are aware of the current research on depression and mood disorder drugs and this is helpful in determining dosage levels and in reducing side effects. If a person does not respond to a certain type of medication, a psychiatrist, like other physicians, has an extensive list of alternative drugs to choose from.

Finding a psychiatrist may be difficult, particularly in rural or sparsely populated areas. During the last fifteen years the number of good psychiatrists has been decreasing. One of the contributing factors to this decline is sheer economics.

It costs a lot of money to run a practice and to hire office support staff. Even though most psychiatrists charge $125 per hour and up for their services they still make less than the traditional M.D.'s. This makes it difficult to attract new doctors into the field.

While their fees may seem high, psychiatrists are highly trained professionals who have spent years in medical school and who can provide their clients with the highest quality of treatment.

Most insurance companies will pay for a psychiatric assessment but it is a good idea to check the mental health provisions of any policy to make sure. It is possible to use up all the allowed benefits in the first few months of treatment.

If economics prohibit the depressed person and the family from seeing a psychiatrist for counseling, it may be possible to see one on a consultant basis. Because of our own financial situation, Dan and I decided to go with this option.

Our insurance coverage only allowed $500 a year in mental health benefits. This limited the amount of time we could afford. We designed a treatment plan with Dan's psychiatrist that allowed Dan to have his medication monitored by the psychiatrist and to receive counseling from a licensed therapist. It provided us with the best of both worlds —medical expertise and psychological therapy at a price we could afford.

44

TREATMENT ALTERNATIVES

Finding the right treatment for depression is like trying to find the prize in a 5-lb box of crackerjacks. For some people, it is an easy process; for others, the search can be grueling and exhausting and may take years.

There are three major types of treatments used in alleviating depression: psychotherapy, medications and biological treatments.

There are a variety of options in each of these categories. The treatment choice will depend on the outcome of the doctor's evaluation. Sometimes the treatments will be combined to try to meet the specific needs of the depressed person. For example, medication may be used to help regulate the brain chemistry while, at the same time, psychotherapy is initiated to help the depressed person deal with life problems.

Antidepressant Medications

If the depression is severe, antidepressant medication may be an effective treatment. Several types of antidepressants are available to treat depressive disorders. They come in various forms and include: tricyclics, monoamine oxidase (MAO) inhibitors, Lithium and Prozac.

Prozac. Much has been reported recently about the effectiveness of Prozac. It is the medication of choice for many depressed people because of its effectiveness with few side effects. For those people, its relatively high cost is probably well worth it. While thousands of people are helped by it, there are some people for whom Prozac is not effective. Dan was one of them.

Tricyclics. Dan tried these next. There are many different kinds of tricyclic medications that are used to treat depression and anxiety. Some of them can trigger diverse reactions and undesirable side effects. The search to find the right drug is much like throwing the dice and hoping for doubles. Some people get doubles on the first try and the medication works great; others search desperately trying to find the right combination.

Our kitchen cupboard began to look like a pharmaceutical supply house as Dan tried medication after medication. He

45

was not getting better and we were spending literally hundreds of dollars a month on drugs.

There were times when Dan did quit taking the tricyclics because he did not like the side effects. They weren't severe, just inconvenient. Dry mouth (Dan said it felt like his mouth was full of cotton all the time), drowsiness and constipation are the hardest to deal with. For most people, the benefits of the drugs far outweigh the side effects which disappear as the body adjusts to the medication.

Lithium. This is usually prescribed to level out the extreme highs and lows experienced by a person suffering from manic-depression. It sometimes is effective when used for people who have a severe depression. A recent study of the National Institute of Mental Health reported that 70 percent of the people who suffer from manic-depression were helped by Lithium. As with all drugs, there are some people who do not respond to Lithium but do respond to other drugs.

MAOs. Another choice in medications is a group of antidepressants called MAO inhibitors. Most doctors are reluctant to put people on MAOs because of the fairly strict dietary restrictions that must be followed. People who are taking MAOs should not eat any aged, fermented or pickled foods. This eliminates many cheeses, red wine, beer and certain processed foods. Doctors can provide their patients with a complete list.

Also, no cold medications should be taken along with this medication without consulting with a doctor. Certain medications will interact with the MAO and can cause blood pressure to go sky high and, if not controlled, may have fatal consequences.

In our search for the right medication, we found that the MAOs were the ones that worked best for Dan. Even though they had many restrictions, they were the first drug that actually pulled him out of his "black hole." Within a week of taking the drug, he became dramatically better. After two weeks he was a different man.

During this period, Dan and I both learned a lot about antidepressants.

– They are not addictive. People can take these medications for years and not become addicted.

– They are not tranquilizers, pep pills, or sleeping pills. Antidepressants return the brain chemistry to normal.

– Most people need to be on an antidepressant for at least three months to see substantial improvement.

– Antidepressants need to be taken regularly.

– No one should stop taking an antidepressant because they feel better without first discussing it with the doctor. If a depressed person stops taking the medication too soon they may become severely depressed within a short period of time.

– If someone is not depressed, antidepressants won't work. They are not "energy" pills. They will not provide joy to someone who is living in an unbearable situation. They are not "happiness" pills.

– A low dosage of an antidepressant may not be enough. Frequently, a low dosage will not help the depression and a higher dosage will be required before the medication "kicks" in. Too much medication will be noticeable as well and can be dangerous. It is important that medication levels be monitored closely by a doctor.

– It is possible for antidepressants to cure depression. In some people the antidepressant actually may teach the brain's neurons to respond differently. It also may teach the neurons to return to normal and the brain takes over where the medication left off.

– Most antidepressants take one to two weeks to work. If there is no improvement in two weeks, call the doctor.

– It may take as long as two to three days on the medication to determine what reaction an individual will have to it. If any side effects seem to be overwhelming, it may be wise to change medications.

– Never mix antidepressants with other medications without first contacting the doctor.

– Alcohol reduces the effect of antidepressants and should be avoided.

A major mistake we made in dealing with medications was changing them without adequate planning for side effects. Dan switched medications a couple of days before we left on a

47

trip to Atlanta, Georgia. After two days in Atlanta, I could see that he was getting worse. The new medication made him edgy and tense. It distorted his comprehension of distance and direction, and interfered with his driving. After coping for five days, we were both mentally and physically exhausted. As soon as we returned home, Dan went to see the doctor and got his medication changed.

Biological Therapies

Electroconvulsive Therapy. With the advances in medical technology, electroconvulsive therapy (ECT) has become a much more refined and specialized treatment for serious depression. While we all have visions of the horrors of the "shock" treatments of the 1950's, we can rest assured that modern use of ECT is a much more humane and dignified treatment.

Many people who suffer from depression get no help from other methods of treatment and ECT is used as a last resort. The procedure is painless to the patient who is anesthetized and asleep.

Electrodes are placed on the scalp and an electrical current passes through the brain. That current somehow changes the chemistry of the brain. The patient is given a muscle relaxant to minimize muscle reaction during the treatment. In 20 to 30 minutes the treatment is complete and the patient is back in a hospital room. The number of treatments required to alleviate the depression varies. Many people who have tried ECT as a last resort are now living a life they never dreamed was possible for them.

Light Therapy. In the last few years, it has been discovered that thousands of people suffer from a type of depression called "Seasonal Affective Disorder." This kind of depression affects people most in the winter. It has been determined that there is a certain hormone that is affected when we are not exposed to enough light. For people who suffer with this kind of depression, the cure is simply to get more light. This is usually accomplished by sitting in front of bright lights (especially designed for this illness). The light stimulates the hormone and the body chemistry returns to normal. This treatment usually takes weeks but the benefits can be worth the time spent.

A PLAN OF ATTACK

Together, Dan; his psychiatrist; Dale; and I, decided that Dan's treatment should be a combination of medication and psychotherapy. When I felt the doctors were talking over my head and I needed more information about specific treatment strategies or medications, I went to the bookstore and purchased what I believe to be one of the best books on the medical aspects of depression. *The Good News About Depression* by Dr. Dan Gold (Bantam, 1986) is an excellent resource book for families looking for treatment alternatives.

The treatment process can be very gratifying if the medication works right away, and very grueling if there seems to be no treatment that is working. For some depressed people, finding the prize of the appropriate medication in the crackerjack box of alternatives comes quickly but for others, the search may continue for some time. For a few, a treatment combining medication and psychotherapy may not provide the whole answer.

HOSPITALIZATION

Hospitalization of a loved one brings its own mix of emotions. Some depressed people admit themselves; in severe cases, the family has to take action. They may wonder if they did the right thing in admitting the depressed person but, on the other hand, they feel so relieved that the entire family will be getting a break from the stress with which they have probably been living.

Admitting the depressed person to a hospital involves answering innumerable questions and completing mountains of paperwork. It means meeting with counselors, social workers, psychologists, psychiatrists, and representatives of the business office who may want you to make payment arrangements.

Hospitals vary in terms of the treatment programs offered and the length of care provided. Most hospitals will assign a number of different professionals to work with the depressed person. Good insurance coverage is vital. The costs

49

of in-hospital care for depression can be very expensive.

The quality of hospital care also may vary. If possible, families faced with this decision should visit various facilities and talk to the administrators and staff about the care and treatment options available before hospitalizing the depressed family member.

Hospitals provide structured therapy, activities and leisure time. Most have a significant number of rules and regulations that must be followed.

Some depressed people go in and out of hospitals like most of us go to a bank or post office. They are regulars who can't seem to shake the illness. Some stay for a few days and then check themselves out, only to regress and check back in again.

For the families, hospitalization of a depressed person can quickly turn into an extremely stressful situation. The patient may call from the hospital saying irrational things and making demeaning statements to family members, who often have no one to talk to or to confide in. They may have sworn not to tell anyone about the hospitalization.

Visiting the depressed person in the hospital may be difficult for partners and family members. Some people cannot stand to visit because it reminds them of the pain they have endured. The anger and hurt that family members feel gets blended with the stress associated with a hospital and many people choose not to go through the agony that a hospital visit brings.

PSYCHOTHERAPY

Psychotherapy is very effective in the treatment of depression. A therapist serves as a catalyst for the depressed person and the family to help them learn new ways of living. The therapist's goal is to help the client improve personal and social functioning. Therapy is offered to families, couples, and individuals. It usually involves "talking" with the therapist to gain insight into problems. The depressed person often is taught how to make certain behavioral changes that will result in making his life more rewarding and fulfilling. Some therapists delve into the past, looking for reasons why the depressed person is stuck in the present. By looking back at what has happened in the past, a therapist is able to isolate certain incidents that could be contributing to the depression.

A therapist helps the depressed person work through all of the emotions he or she may be feeling on the inside in order to resolve many of the conflicts taking place on the outside.

Dan managed to stay out of the hospital under the condition that I would monitor him at home. We began to feel more positive about the future. We now had two experts—Dan's psychiatrist and Dale—helping us to understand and cope with the illness. I was learning more and more about depression and Dan was feeling better just knowing a potential drug might work. We hardly had time to enjoy this small step forward before we were forced to face our next challenge—how to pay for all this help.

6 | Paying For It All: "I Only Get Depressed When I Pay The Bill."

No one can prepare you for the costs involved with a chronic illness. When a depressed spouse or family member cannot work, it may result in a tremendous loss of income. This, in turn, can lead to a drop in the standard of living, another stress on an already fully stressed-out family.

The financial part of the commitment to overcoming the depression begins with the first therapy session. Most mental health professionals ask that payment for services be made in full at the time of service. Usually, a receptionist will handle the payment and schedule a time for the next appointment. In small private practices, however, the therapist or doctor may handle the payment and schedule the next appointment.

THE THERAPEUTIC ALLIANCE

It is very important that clients know and understand that the mental health professional they see is providing a service and not just doing a favor for a friend. The clinician has spent years in college and thousands of hours in training to understand the complex psychological processes of the human mind and body.

Clients share many things with their therapists, including their innermost thoughts and feelings. A clinician genuinely cares about his clients and spends the hour-long sessions devotedly working with their problems. Even though, at times, this may feel like friendship, in fact, it is a professional relationship. Friends are people who choose to spend time together having fun pursuing mutual interests, participating in family activities and sharing thoughts and feelings.

A clinician is a person with a family and social life built around people outside of his or her professional practice.

Even though we had the same relationship with our therapist that we had with our doctor or dentist or any professional, it seemed difficult for us to accept the idea of paying a fee just for "sitting and talking."

ASSESSING THE WORTH

It always seemed easier to justify writing checks to Dan's doctor and to our local pharmacy for medications than paying for the counseling. While some people believe that "you don't need to pay someone to figure out your life for you," these same people will gladly pay someone to figure out why the oil is leaking out of their car.

"After all, you need the car to go to work. You just can't have a car leaking oil all over the driveway."

Depressed people are a lot like cars. If they are too depressed to even get out of bed, they aren't working right. While broken cars sometimes leak oil on the driveway, depressed people may leak blood all over themselves and their families from a botched suicide attempt. Depressed people need to hire the expertise necessary to help them fix themselves so they can cope in this world.

When depression is the problem, it is important to find good help and to pay for it. When you write a check for therapy, you are paying for a service to help you grow and heal.

JUGGLING THE BANK ACCOUNTS

Methods of payment vary from clinician to clinician. Some therapists and most doctors can bill your health insurance provider if your policy includes some form of mental health coverage. Others provide options such as sliding scale rates based on a client's income. Still others just charge a flat hourly rate.

The rate and payment method can be determined prior to the first appointment. If a depressed person's financial situation is bleak and he can't afford to pay the regular fee but is in dire need of help, some doctors and therapists are willing to work out alternative arrangements.

COST-EFFECTIVE TREATMENT ALTERNATIVES

Most current research shows that depression can be greatly helped by individual and family psychotherapy, but if it is just financially impossible to consider that option, there are other types of counseling available that may serve the needs of the depressed person and his or her family. Group therapy is one option.

A variety of groups deal with addictive behaviors such as alcoholism or substance abuse. In many communities, there are support groups for depression. These groups usually can be found through local mental health associations. Support groups meet at various locations, and they sometimes have a licensed counselor who facilitates the group. The number of people participating greatly affects the amount of sharing that can be done within the group. Most groups are composed of less than 25 people. Any more than that and the group experience tends to lose its effectiveness.

Groups provide a safe atmosphere in which the depressed person and the family members can share feelings with other people who are going through the same experiences. An advantage of the group experience over traditional one-on-one therapy is in the experiential expressive role-playing. Members of the group can act as members of a family, for example, and role-play depressive episodes in a person's life. Role-playing allows depressed people to see from the outside how their behavior may be affecting other members of their families.

A major disadvantage of group therapy is that there may not be enough time to work through specific issues relevant to the individual. There are many people in the group who have many different problems and group sessions are limited to one or two hours allowing only enough time to discuss maybe three or four issues.

Sometimes, people may go away from the group therapy session feeling that a lot of thoughts have been stirred up but that it really didn't help define and overcome the problems with depression any better than what they could have done on their own.

Well-structured groups can do effective work in some areas. For a depressed person with limited financial resources, it is worth taking the time to check into these options and visit a group or two to see how they work.

THE WISH TO BE SAVED

Dan and I chose to go to the traditional type of one-on-one individual/family counseling because, after our first session with Dale, we both felt good about him. Dan was so depressed that the group experience probably would not have worked well for us.

Our journey into therapy had begun and we hoped the many changes we would have to undergo would bring us intact to the place where we could begin a new life. We were not in great shape financially but we decided that paying for counseling would be a positive investment in our relationship. We agreed to make some sacrifices in our family expenses so that we could pay for the help we so badly needed.

No matter which type of therapy the depressed person and the family choose, they are are going to have to invest a significant amount of money. The cost of therapy, however, is much less than what the ultimate costs, both human and financial, will be if the illness drags on.

Before we began therapy, our family already had experienced a frightening downward trend our lifestyle. Dan's absence from work had severely reduced our family income. All the money we had left after paying our regular household and living expenses went to pay for medications, doctors' appointments and therapy.

We began to cut out all the "extras" and to channel our funds into helping Dan help himself. Once we had made the commitment, we were in for the challenge of a lifetime in our attempt to beat the depression, end the nightmare and rebuild our lives.

Section II

ENDING THE NIGHTMARE

7 | Beginning to End

"It isn't for the moment you are struck that you need courage but for the long uphill climb back to sanity, faith and security."

– Anne Morrow Lindbergh –

TURNING POINT

At some point in the progression of the illness, either the depressed person or the well family members decide that things cannot continue as they have been. This is the first step in a long journey through the process of "ending," making the decision that the old life isn't working anymore, that the existing conflict patterns are destroying the family.

When Dan attempted suicide, I knew our lives had reached this turning point. There was no way that we could return to the way we were. It was clear that we were destroying each other and the madness had to end.

I wanted to help Dan get over his depression and I

61

wanted to stop all the trauma we had been going through as a family but I was paralyzed by the fear of change. Even though our relationship was destructive, it was all I knew and there was a part of me that hated to let go of it. It was familiar and, bizarre as it seems, it was in a way comfortable.

The scary part of letting go of our destructive family patterns and trying to build a more satisfying and productive family life was the transitional state of "not knowing."

I had depended on Dan to meet all of my needs—physical, emotional, financial. I made virtually no major decisions about my life. We always did what Dan wanted to do. We went where he wanted to go. We lived the way he wanted to live.

Now, Dan and I stood at a crossroads—looking back at the unhappy though familiar past and feeling drawn to the unknown and uncertain but, perhaps, better and more satisfying future. Like many other families living with depression, we had arrived at this place because of a crisis. Because of Dan's suicide attempt, we were compelled to seek a new direction and this was the point at which we recognized we had to "end" our old way of living.

Endings often happen because of a turn of events. It may be as simple as a change of thought or as serious as a suicide attempt. Everyone goes through the different stages of the ending process in a different way. No matter how you approach it, it always feels uncomfortable.

THE THERAPY BEGINS

After Dan had been on his medication for about two weeks, his mood started to lift and our relationship began to stabilize. It was clear that we both carried emotional scars from the constant battle zone we had been living in. Neither one of us could forget all the emotional and psychological pain we had been through. Beginning therapy was a step we had to take to end the unhappiness of the past.

After the initial sessions, which were devoted to determining the extent of the illness, Dale, Dan and I began trying to unravel the past and discover the possible causes of the depression.

We spent several therapy sessions talking about our childhoods, how we ended up together and how the events of our past were now affecting our marriage and triggering Dan's depression. By listening to each other talk about our pasts, Dan and I gained a deeper insight and a new awareness of who we "really" were. It was surprising to find out how much we did not know about each other.

FIRE AND ICE

Dan was the oldest child in a large family. His parents were very religious and the children were raised in strict accordance with church principles. Dan had a difficult time living with his family's religion. He hated to be "told" what to do and he rebelled against his parents and the church.

Even as a child, Dan thought about suicide. He said that when he was a 7th grader, he hoped he would die. He told a story of going into the bathroom, leaning against the bathroom door with a knife pointed at his chest and praying that someone would push the door open so the knife would stab him through his heart.

As he got older, Dan's thoughts of suicide increased, but he never had the courage to follow through. He said he didn't have any close relationships with anyone in his family and did not feel comfortable at home.

He began to spend more and more time away from home. He moved in and out of the house. He would stay at a friend's place and then go home for awhile. He went to live with his grandmother and tried out college. That didn't work out and he returned home again.

He spent the next two years in Canada doing church work. After he returned home, he developed new friendships and his church began to take a backseat to the "real" life he was living. Eventually, the gap between Dan and his parents widened.

He moved in with one of his new friends and began to drink and party a lot. He worked all day and partied all night. I don't think I ever saw him sober. So, why did I get involved with him? I had an agenda of my own from the family I grew up in. In many ways we were a "perfect" match.

I grew up in a small family, my mom, dad, myself and a younger brother. My parents had a miserable relationship that was truly hopeless from the start. They were married out of obligation and stayed that way for 13 long, chaotic years. They fought constantly. As a child, I would sit on my bed listening to them argue for hours and hours. I remember feeling terrified and very alone.

I was always trying to take care of my parents and make everything okay for them so they would not argue. I had a hard time dealing with my emotions. I was overweight in grade school and was constantly harassed by the other kids. My self-esteem was almost non-existent.

As I got older, I lost the weight but gained more problems. My parents had divorced and I became the "other" parent to my younger brother. My mother had a job that required her to work long hours. I took care of my brother and tried to take care of the house.

When I was 17, my mother moved to another state and my 15-year-old brother and I got an apartment and tried to survive on our own. I went to high school and worked. My brother was a diabetic and it took everything I had emotionally, physically and financially to keep us afloat.

After a few months, my mother returned home and my brother went back to living with her. I started college and moved into an apartment with a friend from work. It was nice to come home and have someone to talk to. My roommate was seven years older than me, but it seemed as if we were the same age. I started to date and one night, I was invited to a party . . . and I met Dan.

I had been invited to the party by a friend who had left the address on my doorstep. When I got there, I found that my friend had already left but the host invited me in and began to introduce me. Dan grabbed my arm and insisted on pouring me a drink. I had never tasted hard liquor before but Dan convinced me that it was great. I drank two 10-ounce glasses full of vodka and limeade. After the second glass, I knew I was going to be sick. I left the apartment and tried to get to my car. I never made it.

My friend who had invited me to the party lived in the same apartment complex. I found his apartment and lay down on the sidewalk in front of the door. Everything was spinning. The next thing I knew, I was inside the apartment and waking up to an alarm clock that said 10:45 a.m. "Good morning," said Dan, the generous bartender from the previous night's party.

I found out that he was actually my friend's roommate and that he had come home to find me "passed out" on his doorstep. He had carried me into his apartment and put me on the couch for the night. I talked to him for about two minutes that morning and grabbed my purse and left. I was very embarrassed and ashamed of what had happened.

Dan and I saw each other again a few nights later and that weekend he asked me to go with him to church. I thought his request was bizarre, considering his reputation and his drinking ability, but we went and I met his family. After church we drove around. He asked me if I would like to go with him to Canada in two weeks. I told him I would love to go but I didn't have the money. He said it was okay, the trip was on him.

He seemed to need me and I needed the vacation so I agreed. We had a good time on the trip. He was loving and considerate. He took me shopping and bought me presents. He was gentle and thoughtful. He seemed sensitive and had a great sense of humor. He was so different from the other macho men I had dated. Even though he acted wild, drove fast and drank a lot, I thought I could handle it. His chaotic and rebellious style was appealing and I liked him a lot.

After that trip we spent every hour we could together . He moved into my apartment and took care of my bills. I had struggled for so long to stay in college while keeping the rent and the other bills paid, it was a relief to have someone take care of me for a change, someone who seemed to care so much about me.

Dan and I were married exactly three months from the day we first met. I had no clue as to who he really was and what pain he was suppressing by his drinking. He had no idea about my troubled past. I was fire and he was ice. Together, we were a mess of charred and cold embers from our burned-out pasts.

The early years of our marriage were difficult. As time went on Dan's drinking and his depression increased. The more he drank the less productive he became.

I went back to school because I knew that if his drinking continued there was a good chance that he would not be able to work. He spent many days at home on the sofa. He just did not care about anything that had to do with work. To him it was just one more obligation.

Dan rarely took a shower or combed his hair when he was depressed. He would come home from work covered with dirt and grease. The grease ruined our furniture, carpeting and walls. He didn't care. That's how he was and I could take it or leave it.

So here we were, nine years later, looking back at our lives and trying to understand how all that past history could be affecting us today.

8 | Dysfunctional Families

THERE ARE NO PERFECT FAMILIES

Dale asked me one night if I could describe my ideal family. I said, "Sure, I'll tell you what I always wanted . . . ."

I could describe it exactly. A perfect family had six—count' em,—six perfect children who always looked adorable and never had so much as a dirty face. The husband and wife looked and acted as if they had just stepped off the top of the wedding cake. The family dog was cute and lovable. Even the neighbors were warm, friendly and perfect.

My envisioned family had an excellent housekeeper who took care of the kids, the shopping, the housework and the laundry. The wife spent her days working as a volunteer in the community. The husband was a highly-respected architect. The biggest problem this ideal family had was where to go on vacation.

If this ideal family sounds familiar, it should. Their name was Brady and, with millions of other Americans, I watched them every week on television. Kids who grew up in the early 1970's all wanted to live just like "The Brady Bunch."

The Brady kids are now in their thirties and are coping with a world that in no way resembles the ideal world they thought would always be there. For their real-life counterparts, the world can be an even greater disappointment. The Brady family didn't deal with sexual abuse or child abandonment. The Brady kids never lacked in the love or self-esteem department. They had the perfect life we all wanted.

The Brady Bunch was an imaginary family, images on a screen, and the rest of us were real people living in the real world struggling to understand why we weren't just like the Bradys.

COLLISIONS OF UNREALISTIC EXPECTATIONS WITH REALITY

Television created unrealistic expectations and many of us have grown up believing that if we only did this or that or behaved in a certain way or if we only had a nicer home or a new car, then we would really have the happy family life. In our culture, if we want to consider ourselves worthwhile and successful people, it seems we must possess certain attributes that I have heard referred to as the five B's—Beauty, Brains, Bank Accounts, Business (producing, achieving, accomplishing) and Belonging (conforming).

If your family is beautiful, highly educated, with six-figure incomes, exciting careers and lots of love, you are doing okay in the U.S.A. I wanted this kind of life for myself and my family and I worked overtime trying to make us just like the Brady Bunch. Hollywood had created the perfect "image" of a family and I was trying to recreate it at home.

When I got into therapy I spent a lot of time initially, trying to uphold a facade of this dream family life. Like most therapists, Dale was not fooled by appearances and he was able to see right through my pretense. He knew that behind that facade of "we are the Brady Bunch," there were problems galore.

The human spirit is naturally drawn to the comfort of a family. From the day of our birth we learn what it means to belong to a family. Our families provide us with emotional nurturing and socialization skills that help us to get along with other people.

This loving support is vital to our emotional development. The family shares the task of transforming a biological organism into a fully-functioning human being. An infant grows up with the realities taught inside the family system. If a baby is lucky, it is raised in a loving and nurturing family. Many of us were not so lucky and our basic needs went unmet.

We all need to feel safe, to have a sense of belonging, to be touched and held and cuddled. We need to be heard. We need to know that we are unconditionally loved and that we will be accepted no matter what we do. We need to be listened to. We need support and encouragement. We need to feel a sense of accomplishment, and we need to have the freedom to grow and change.

For many children, these basic needs go unmet because their parents lack the necessary information and education that would enable them to be more skillful parents.

Unfortunately, we live in a society that does not educate future parents about the fundamentals of good parenting. While we spend hours in classrooms learning the basic principles of a future career, few of us ever take a class on childrearing, which is something we can expect to be doing for at least 18 to 20 years of our life. New parents tend to rely on what they learned about raising children from their own parents. Those past experiences may not have been pleasant but for many young parents it is the only knowledge available to them.

Consequently, many people grow up in what is commonly known as a dysfunctional family. Some estimates indicate that up to 95 percent of American families are dysfunctional in some way.

TROUBLED PEOPLE/MESSED-UP LIVES

Dysfunctional families are families out of balance. They suffer from the "too much" syndrome. It can be too much of something negative like too much drinking, too much abuse, too much materialism, or too much religion. It can be too much of something normally thought of as positive – too much love for children (none is left for the couple and the marriage deteriorates), too much love of the spouses for each other (children are abandoned).

Dysfunctional families have a tremendous problem potential. The problems can come in chaotic packages or calm packages. They can be very obvious or very subtle. Day-to-day life for dysfunctional families is stressful. The communication among family members is poor. There is usually a lot of conflict (stated or unstated) between family members. There is a great amount of game playing and manipulation. Love is conditional. "I'll love you if. . . ."

There is a lack of trust in dysfunctional families because no one knows what is going to happen next. There may be a lot of judging among family members. There may be fear. The longer the dysfunction goes on, the harder it is to fix. Some families are so dysfunctional they literally destroy themselves.

After Dan's depression was diagnosed, I got lost in a lot of why questions. Why me? Why this? Why that? Why do I stay? Why does he act this way? Why can't he get better? Why can't I fix him or her?

For a depressed person, the answers to some of the why questions may be linked to the child that depressed person was in the past and also to the child that the other adults in the family were. The child that existed in the past was like a video recorder. Every experience, positive or negative, that we have had in our lives is stored in the subconscious mind. Each of us carries within ourselves that child from the past. Pain that we experienced at the age of seven can still be affecting us at the age of 37 or 47 or 87!

As Dan and I began to confront our pasts, it was clear to us that we both had grown up in dysfunctional families and now we were in danger of creating another dysfunctional family for our own children.

DIGGING UP BONES

Yesterday's events have a profound effect on current problems. Yesterday's smoldering coals—the unresolved conflict, mixed messages and unexamined feelings of the past—create today's fires. Depressed adults either work out their inner conflicts or they live them out. What we deny from yesterday may continue to cause pain today. Who we were as children is who we are today unless we make a conscious decision to change.

Families entering therapy often ask, Why do I need to talk so much about the past when all that is over and done with now?

This seems like a reasonable response. However, most of us still carry around potentially lethal garbage from past relationships. The actual painful incident may be over but the psychological effect is still present. Until a person can deal with the pain of the past and finish it, he will be emotionally suspended in time and unable to move on.

Children who grow up in dysfunctional families collect lots of information about who they are from how other people treat them. Our self-concepts are built or shattered as a result of the way we were viewed and cared for while we were growing up. These early life experiences greatly contribute to the kind of person we become as adults.

All our past experiences are buried in our memory vaults. If there are some bad experiences that we have never dealt with, and we have had no opportunity to grieve our losses of the past and recover from the anguish we have gone through, we may find ourselves repeating painful experiences again and again in our relationships of the present. The old video tapes from our childhood are always with us. As an adult, under stress, we sort through the old video tapes for solutions to our problems.

Growing up in a dysfunctional family is like living with a keg of dynamite sitting in the kitchen. Everybody is aware of the problem and they know that it could explode at any moment without warning. Because the situation is so stressful the family members begin to withdraw. They shut down their feelings and lock up their fears.

Children from dysfunctional families have learned not to trust or believe in anything. There is no consistency in their family life. They learn to accept negative reactions and even to expect them. If they get any recognition or reward, they may not know how to react. They may, in fact, react negatively to positive feedback.

Confronted constantly with conflict (stated or unstated), children in dysfunctional families become very good "radar" detectors. They watch every action of each person in the family. They are able to accurately predict what is going to happen and describe what the patterns have been in the past. To a child conflicts are very big and unsettling regardless of how they are manifested.

Children who have grown up in environments that are unbalanced, unstable, and constantly in crisis come to believe that living in a constant whirlwind of problems, conflicts and stress is normal. They adapt themselves to the situation and become addicted to chaos. They learn well the art of crisis creation. They subconsciously want a crisis to guide their lives and if they don't have one, they create one. As adults, they may create crisis after crisis and destroy relationship after relationship.

Peaceful situations in a family do not fit the "pattern" of chaos they have learned growing up. Calmness and serenity is scary and uncomfortable. They are comfortable with what they know, even if it is crazy, and they often become frightened when they find themselves living in a peaceful environment they don't understand. Children who grow up in these "nightmare" family situations become very good at denial – pretending things are different than they are, so that they can keep some kind of sanity.

The illusions children raised in a dysfunctional family grow up with are difficult to change. The child within believes that if it is not loved, it cannot survive. As an adult, when we encounter someone who is angry or upset with us or when we are under severe stress, we go back into our child state and become like a five-year-old saying, "Oh, no, I'm bad . . . they are angry . . . they will abandon me and I am going to

72

die." When we are frightened and feel afraid, we act in ways we would never act normally. We act on illusions instead of reality.

Mental, physical, or sexual abuse in a family often results in tremendous illusion-building by children. If a child grows up mentally and physically abused, he feels guilt, shame and despair—guilt about what he may have done to deserve the abuse and shame, about who or what he is, or about what the family is. The despair comes from a feeling of powerlessness. "I cannot change the way they treat me . . . I can't change the way they act . . . I always do it wrong . . . I am a bad person."

The longer the abuse goes on, the more believable the illusions become. Some of the most powerful and persistent illusions are reinforced by constant negative self-talk. The inner child is battered and believes these distorted thoughts about himself. The adult the child continues to believe these illusions are true and is depressed and confused.

ILLUSIONS

Some of the illusions that a depressed person may have carried over from childhood include:

Illusion: *I am bad, selfish, no good!*
Fact: We are all very good.
Illusion: *This pain will go on forever.*
Fact: The pain of the past does not have to continue.
Illusion: *I am helpless and have no control over my life.*
Fact: I am not a victim; I am in control of my own life.
Illusion: *People and events make me feel bad.*
Fact: I can decide for myself how I respond to people and events.
Illusion: *Everyone else controls my life.*
Fact: Each person controls his own life.
Illusion: *The kind of family I grew up in is the only kind of family I deserve.*
Fact: I can work to create my own healthy and happy family life.

It is vital in the treatment of depression to try to unlock the past and separate the illusions from the facts. This is a slow and painful process and should be done with the help of a therapist.

UNLOCKING THE PAST

The first step in dealing with depression is trying to figure out who you are, where you have been, and end the past. Recovery from depression means ending the pain. Ending the pain patterns involves clearing relationships of all the destructive patterns that hold loved ones away from each other. It is like weeding a garden in order to grow better crops.

Many depressed adults have been depressed kids. These children grow up and seem to function in society fairly well for a while, sometimes a fairly long while. Then, something— perhaps a significant life event—triggers the old video tapes from the past and the person's childhood self returns to haunt the subconscious mind of the adult. But no one wants to love, cuddle, and rock a difficult, angry adult and, consequently, the childhood self experiences rejection once again.

Depressed adults find it difficult to function in interpersonal relationships. They tend to mess up or destroy everything positive in their lives. If they seem to have no problems, they create some. They form self-destructive patterns and have no idea why they do so. The child they once were has been hurt and the adult now must work through the pain of the past in order to heal the present life.

We tend to seek out what we know, what is familiar, even if it's not good for us. If our inner child only knew pain and suffering, failure and abandonment then, subconsciously, as an adult we feel that is what we deserve. We continue to "fall into" situations that cause us pain and heartbreak, and we never understand why.

Our parents were our wizards. As children we didn't have the ability to distinguish between truth and fictional comments. We believed whatever our parents told us. If they told us we were bad, we were. When children who have internalized these negative messages evolve into adults

74

suffering from severe depression, their old illusions can tear their new family apart.

After several weeks of work in therapy it became apparent that Dan and I had been drawn to each other to try to fill the voids left from our childhoods. We had rarely experienced peace, love, or happiness in our original family environment, we didn't look for partners who would help us find it.

Like many other adults who were raised in dysfunctional families, we each began a marriage with a person who was capable of creating an environment that stimulated our own inner conflicts. Now, we were creating with our own children another generation of dysfunctional family life.

It seemed to me that Dan's inner child was looking for a security blanket, something that would keep him safe. He had to have the security to make him happy. He was dependent on me to make him happy and wanted to have complete control over me.

My inner child was always trying to please him. Of course, I could never do everything he wanted me to do in the exact way he wanted it done so the "prize" of having him love me was always just out of reach.

Many of us marry someone who helps fill in the gaps we have in our own self-worth. Opposites attract, outgoing to the shy, the strong to the weak, the assertive to the non-assertive. We find people who have the qualities we lack, fall in love with them and then, later, resent our partners for having these qualities. The child within knows the desperate need for the qualities it lacks. In relationships, that need begins as, "I need you" and then turns into, "I resent having to need you."

Dan was quiet and reserved. He married his opposite— free-spirited, outgoing and fun-loving Kellie. At first, he found my energy and enthusiasm appealing. However, the longer we were married and the more depressed he became, the more he perceived those same qualities as irresponsible and extremely undependable.

Through therapy, Dan and I each came to understand the needs of our own inner child. Once we understood those needs, we were better able to recognize our individual problem areas. We found we could begin to change certain patterns in our relationship. We could admit to ourselves and to each other, "I don't want to live like that anymore."

None of us is condemned forever to our childhood pain, but depressed people often lock themselves up in it. Many families spend their lives entrapped in patterns of the past. It doesn't have to be that way. Once we have determined what has happened to the depressed individual in the past, we can then focus attention on what is happening in the family today.

Looking back is not easy. Some depressed people are so wounded by what happened to them as children that they are afraid to open up all those "hurts" and feel the pain again.

Imagine a depressed person sitting inside a big box. The box has three solid sides and one side with a huge glass door. The glass door has hundreds of locks—illusions that have been put there by the depressed person over the years to protect himself from the pain and suffering experienced in the outside world. He can look out on the world through the big glass door but he won't let anyone in. It is too great a risk. He has been hurt enough and does not want to get hurt again.

The only way for anyone else to open all the locks is to find the keys that fit them. These keys have been lost long ago in the past and have to be slowly searched for and then gently turned to open the locks. The therapist guides the depressed person through the past, reveals the keys, and gradually the depressed person gains the courage to open the locks.

Eventually, the therapist or a family member is allowed to come into the box to help the depressed person work on the problems that have kept him isolated and afraid. Once the depressed person feels safe, he can begin to step out of the box and back into the outside world. It is hard work, taking those first steps that lead out of the nightmare. When recovery from depression is the goal, then the hard work is worth the effort and brings tremendous benefits.

Dan and I decided to end the disruptive, unhealthy activities and interactions that were the side-effects of his depression so that we could begin to live as normal well-functioning human beings.

Through therapy we were able to look back at where we had been and begin to unlock the locks that had kept us in the nightmare.

9 | Living With Someone Who Is Depressed

WHOSE LIFE IS THIS, ANYWAY?

Living with someone who is depressed is like living a nightmare. Depressed people are in a constant state of change. They don't know what they want. They are constantly searching for happiness.

Anxiety and tension are constant companions and families become frantic and unorganized. Information provided by professionals about the depression seems unrelated to the day-to-day problems of living with the illness. The family absorbs little of what they are being told.

Our family was no different. When I began to look at how this illness was affecting us, I was overwhelmed with sadness. I felt as though we had no control—depression had come in and rolled through our lives like a freight train. It ran over us and left us lying in pieces along the tracks, trying to deal with the pain and heartache it had brought us.

There were many days when I seemed to be living in a torture chamber. I just wanted to make the pain go away for all of us. Through therapy, Dale was trying to help everyone in the family put the pieces of our lives back together. He guided us through our current crisis (whatever it happened to be that week) and helped us to cope with our day-to-day living.

After suffering for years from the illness, depressed people tend to fall into certain negative thought patterns first identified by Dr. Aaron Beck and called cognitive distortions. These include:

Over-generalization. Believing if it happened once it will happen again.

"She never does anything right, she never has and never will."

"She stayed late after class last week so she'll do that every night."

"Give her $2 and she'll take $100."

"If she gets to spend 20 minutes with her friends, she'll want to stay for two weeks."

"If someone doesn't control her she will be out of control."

Selective Perception. Seeing only the negative and discounting anything positive. While I was in school, I was selected for inclusion in *Who's Who in American Colleges and Universities*. This prestigious award is given to outstanding students who have made significant contributions to their University. I was to receive my award at a formal ceremony and I wanted Dan to attend.

The ceremony was scheduled to start at 4:00 p.m., and Dan didn't arrive home from work until 3:30. He walked in the door covered with grease and filled with anger. We argued and he told me that he could not stand the fact that I was receiving an award and he was not. After all, he said, he had worked damn hard to help me through school.

The entire day was ruined for me. We arrived late for the ceremony. Dan smoked and complained the whole time. I sat and thought about what a contrast we were. He was from his world of the dark and I was basking in my world of the light. I felt miserable because he was so miserable. I wanted him to share my joy and my pride . . . he wanted no part of it.

The minute the program was over he took off without so much as a goodbye and went back to his shop. His self-esteem was so low that he simply could not be happy for me. "You got an award! You're better than I am! I'm no good!" On what was supposed to be one of the most memorable days of my life, I was feeling sorry about getting the award because of the toll it was taking on my depressed husband.

A year later we went through the same hell when I presented a paper I had written to a statewide education conference. The awards for that competition were to be presented at a Sunday morning breakfast following the judging. Dan would not talk about my paper or the awards ceremony. I went by myself to the breakfast and won first place. I sat alone among strangers. I had won the top honor and I had no one there to share it with me. I smiled, gave a short thank-you speech and sat down.

After the breakfast, I walked out to my car and found I had a flat tire. The tire matched my mood. I called Dan to ask him to help me change the tire but he had gone fishing.

Mind Reading / Projecting. Due to the nature of the illness, the depressed person's thoughts can be distorted. If someone frowns or says something blunt, they assume the worst. "They are rejecting me . . . I hate that S.O.B . . . that woman is a real bitch . . . she thinks she's so great."

Predicting the Future. Depressed individuals tend to predict the future based on their distorted thoughts. "This medication will be just like the last one, it will never work." "Those kids are never going to learn to turn off the lights, they are brats."

KEEPING SECRETS

As a family, we faced a mixed bag of problems, concerns and self-defeating behaviors. The first one we tackled in therapy was keeping secrets, a form of denial.

Family secrets are tightly guarded by the depressed person and the family around him or her. Family secrets are a way to keep the depressed person safe. The family feels very protective about their depressed relative and they want to do what they think will help him get better.

Dan's depression was our family's tightly-guarded secret. We lied for him, covered up for him and made excuses for his inappropriate actions.

The depressed person in the family may blame everyone else for his own misery. If it's not the spouse and kids, it's the boss, or it's the job that gets the blame, or the bills or the church or whatever, but it is never his own fault.

It's like the old adage, "You can't see the forest for the trees." Depressed people exhibit all kinds of signs and symptoms of the illness but they can't see them because they are right in the middle of the pain.

Family members see it all and live with it 24 hours a day. They see every tree in the forest, every symptom and sign, but they may not be able to define the forest as depression. So they deny it exists and try to work around it.

It's easy to get caught up in a web of denial. The family denies that anything is wrong. After all, look at what some of the other people they know are living with. When the neighbor's husband is cheating on his wife, a friend's son has just committed an armed robbery, or a colleague at work is dying of cancer, a spouse's depression seems to be a small problem in comparison.

DENYING THE REALITY

The depressed person's family begins to create its own reality. That reality is not the truth, but it works for a while. Denying the truth somehow seems to make us feel better.

Spouses of depressed persons often may have come from some kind of a dysfunctional background themselves. As a child, they may have lived through much worse situations than they are living with now. Consequently, they have a greater tolerance for the depressed person's inappropriate behavior.

The well spouse of a depressed person begins to take on most of the responsibility for the family. He or she pays the bills and makes sure everyone is fed, clothed and otherwise taken care of. Everything in the house or on the job becomes orderly and efficient to offset the emotional turmoil that is otherwise taking place. The responsible person in the family wants to make everything "okay" for the depressed person and the other family members and ends up taking care of everyone except himself or herself.

When Dan failed to function and could not do all of his work, I picked up where he left off but soon I was running on empty and began to resent every minute of it. I became a stressed-out workaholic and a nag. My puffy cheeks, messed-up hair, and tired eyes communicated my feelings of dejection and hopelessness.

What I thought was loving behavior was not that at all. I took responsibility for Dan and his illness, I tried to make him change, I told him constantly what he was doing was wrong. There were days when I told him, "You're right. You are worthless!" I thought I was doing him a favor.

When Dan created a major problem, I refrained from talking to him about it, because I felt he couldn't "take it" and I didn't want to hurt him. I avoided arguments because peace at any price was better than telling the truth and accepting the consequences. My motto became, "I can't have what I really want . . . so I might as well go along."

Out of love, family members will cover for a depressed person who cannot work—lying to each other, if necessary, to keep the peace. A wife may lie to her husband and say their son has been job hunting during the day when the reality is that he spent the day in bed sleeping. She knows that her husband will be upset by his son's behavior so she gently denies reality because she loves her husband and her depressed son and doesn't want to be responsible for the conflict the truth might create.

The mother may feel embarrassed by her son's actions. It's humiliating for her to admit that he won't "snap out of it" and "go do something productive with his life" when all her friends' kids are in school or have full-time jobs.

It is embarrassing for a husband to admit his wife is depressed and has spent the past three weeks in a treatment center talking about suicide, crying and just giving up for no apparent reason. He is sure no one would understand and might even blame him for his wife's depression.

It was embarrassing for me to attend a social function and then to watch Dan lean on the walls at a friend's house and make negative comments all night. I could never enjoy a social event because I was always on guard, always watching Dan, always checking to see if he was okay, always waiting for some blow-up or argument to take place. After a while, it just got easier to stay home.

Families need to have a certain amount of stability and security. Spouses want to love and respect each other. Children want to admire their parents. This is the ideal. For a family affected by depression, it's difficult to admit to the world that this is not the way things are. If Mom suffers from depression and never gets out of bed, the kids will cover for her by fixing their own breakfast and getting themselves off to school—hoping that someday things will change and Mom's depression will go away.

If the depressed person forgets a birthday, families compensate, "Oh, it doesn't really matter, it's not important anyway." Depression becomes a family secret that lives behind closed doors.

Many depressed people use lying as a form of denial. Dan's lying created a lot of problems for him as well as for the family. He couldn't remember which lie he told and to whom he told it. It was humiliating for him and for me when I discovered the truth of some lie he had told me, or found out about a lie he had told someone else. I lost most of the trust I had in him. I felt like a pawn in a chess game as he used his lies to manipulate and move me around to where he wanted me to be.

FEELING BAD . . . PROJECTING BLAME

Once we stopped denying that the illness existed, the guilt set in. People who are depressed feel bad and unworthy of anything. They feel that they are despicable and that they have let other people down. They know they have hurt other people. When they begin to understand how they have been abusing their families they can't stand to live with themselves.

82

The guilt makes them feel even worse than their actions do. They may even take on guilt that is not appropriate. Like a butterfly collector, whenever they see or hear something that reminds them of their own guilt, they reach out and grab it in their big net and then haul it home for safekeeping.

They feel as if everything they do turns out wrong. Then, they get more depressed and feel even more guilt. They may reach a point when the guilt becomes more than they can handle and they start a process therapists call projection. They begin to project the guilty feelings they have about themselves on to anyone close to them. They begin to blame, blaming someone else for not making perfect coffee, for not spending more time with the children, for not earning enough money, or for anything else that pops into their heads. This allows them to avoid confronting their own problems. They disqualify anything positive the other family members do for them saying, "You did it because you had to (out of guilt) not because you wanted to."

Although no one can actually force another person to feel guilty, a depressed person tries very hard to make the family feel responsible for his illness. Depressed people often set up unrealistic expectations for their spouses and families. Dan would say things like, "I don't care if you are going to college full-time and working a part-time job, that is no excuse for not keeping this house clean and my laundry done. If you loved me you would do it."

Depressed people may point their finger at everyone else's faults and shortcomings in order to avoid facing their own. For family members, it is difficult not to accept the guilt. When they hear day in and day out how rotten they are and how many things they have done wrong, it becomes harder and harder for them to brush off or ignore the criticism and maintain their own self-respect. Family members eventually wear down and slowly begin to believe the depressed person's distorted assessment of them.

I certainly blamed myself for Dan's suffering. The more guilt I felt, the more I tended to draw myself away from him. When I pulled away he was left without support at a time when he needed me the most. He had alienated most of the

83

other people in his life. He had no one else to rely on. I didn't realize it at the time, but I was his sole source of emotional support. And yet, I was the one who caught all of the fallout and was expected to love him anyway.

Families want to make the depressed person happy. They think they can "help" him by doing everything the way the depressed person demands. They make some "trial run" changes and find themselves being controlled by the guilt. They begin to feel that they are the cause of the depression and that if they would just do things a little better, then the depressed person would be in a better mood and the bad times would go away. Unfortunately, the more the family members try to satisfy the depressed person, the more guilty he or she feels, and the worse the depression becomes.

For family members, the guilt projected on to them by the depressed person reinforces many of their own feelings of insecurity or worthlessness. If a depressed person pushes the right buttons, family members can be totally convinced they are completely in the wrong. Some of us panic when our guilt button is pushed and we take it all on, logical or illogical, all that the depressed person will throw our way. This can be carried to absurd lengths.

I can remember one winter morning, getting up and feeling guilty about Dan's truck being covered with snow because he forgot to pull it into the garage the night before. His reaction verged on the hysterical but mine was even more irrational. Not only was I willing to take the blame for not noticing that he had forgotten to put the truck away, I also felt guilty because I had not controlled the weather better so it wouldn't snow on his truck!

Illogical as it was, I accepted all this as my responsibility because I felt it was my job to protect Dan and to keep bad things from happening to him. He kept my guilt going by reminding me once again of all of my faults.

TAKING OVER . . . CARETAKING

Another destructive pattern we developed as a family was "caretaking." Caretaking can be an entanglement trap for

84

everyone involved. When someone is depressed, it is difficult for other family members to trust their competency. They live in fear that the depressed person will crash and screw something up and they will be blamed for it.

I grew up believing it was my job to take care of my family. I did it willingly and always was there. It was "my duty."

Guilt was the driving force behind care-taking. I was taking care of Dan in order to relieve my own guilt. By taking care of him, I was enabling him to remain stuck in his depression.

LIVING TOGETHER . . . ALONE

Despite the other interests in our life—friends, school, hobbies—like many with this illness, we felt isolated and alone. Early morning arguments drained the energy we needed to go about our daily work and to deal with other people. Anticipation of returning home caused tension and anxiety to increase.

Friends asked, "How's the family?" "Fine," I would say. But I stopped inviting people to come to the house and our isolation intensified. As the depression dragged on, the walls around our family began to grow and become more solid. We were not allowing any input to come in from the outside and we were not sharing any of our pain with others.

As the isolation increased, I began to worry and panic around the clock. There was a lot to worry about. Would Dan be able to work next month? Was he going to leave me? What crazy thing would he do next? Is he drinking and driving? Was I going to get beat up? Should I leave? Would that make things better or worse? Is he going to try to kill himself again?

One worry led to another and it became a vicious cycle. The more I worried, the more things I found to worry about. I began to let my mind go wild trying to think of every possible situation that could occur. I played these situations out over and over again in my imagination coming up with every possible alternative solution I could think of for any given situation I might face in the future.

I went to work and I couldn't think clearly. My social life became non-existent. It was impossible to sit through a two-hour movie without worrying about what was going on at home. The more worrying I did the less clearly I thought. Instead of helping to clarify my feelings so that I could plan what to do, worry created anxiety and more psychological pain.

Dan was worried too, although not about the same things. Depending on the severity of his depression, there were times when he was worried about everything in his life or he was so depressed that he did not have the energy to worry about anything.

Most of the time, he tended to go overboard. He worried about things like who was out to cheat him this week or why everyone in the world hated him. He maximized the negative in every situation. It reminded me of the old horror movies where the insects were as big as buildings. Dan saw his problems as big as these surrealistic giant insects and, of course, there was no possible way to manage these giant problems. As our anxiety increased, the worry then began to breed fear.

FEAR — DEPRESSION IS A SCARY ILLNESS

Depression is not something you can see, like the measles or the chickenpox, so we were constantly trying to figure out if the depression was there or not. As well as being unseen, depression can also be contagious. Feeling afraid of the illness is normal. It had devastating effects on Dan and it also affected the rest of us.

One of my greatest fears was that Dan's depression would get much worse before it ever got better. It did. Everyone was denying the depression and trying to act as if everything was okay and yet, at the same time, we were trying to live with intense chaos and unpredictability associated with this illness.

We never knew what to expect from Dan. He could be crying and then laughing and then crying again all within one ten-minute period. Normally a kind and considerate person, Dan became abusive, irritable and intolerant because of the depression. We lived in fear that he would lose control one day

86

and hurt either himself or us. It was hard to trust him. We were afraid he would violate that trust.

I feared being let down again. One more lie, one more disappointment. Dan didn't say what he meant or mean what he said. Why would anyone trust him? As a spouse, I could only hear so many mixed messages before I learned not to trust him anymore.

Dale explained to me that it is very possible for family members to feel afraid and not know why. Since depression is such a closet illness that no one wants to talk about, there is a lot of confusion associated with it. The depressed person doesn't know what's wrong, and the family members aren't sure either. The tension and fear build.

While fear is thriving within the family, it is tearing the depressed person to shreds. They are so afraid of being "found out," and that someone will discover "who they really are," they create huge invisible walls of fear around themselves to hide all the pain they are feeling inside.

Many depressed people want to believe they can handle anything. They want to be like super glue and hold themselves together no matter what. These people find it very difficult to admit they need help. Even though they are hurting terribly inside, they are so afraid of anyone finding out that they are not strong enough to handle their own problems, they put up a shield to keep other people, including loving family members, away. The fear that others may find out they are not perfect keeps them from asking for help. It's almost impossible for them to say, "I want . . . I need . . . I'm hurting . . . ." Often it comes out as "if only . . . you should . . . it's your fault."

Everyone in our family was trying to cope with the fear surrounding Dan's depression, and it drastically affected our ability to make decisions. We learned that when we make decisions out of fear, we are never in control of our lives. The fear, itself, controls us, and it also makes us very angry.

ANGER — A VOLCANIC RAGE

Anger is always a problem when you live with someone who is depressed. Everyone in our family had his or her own anger agenda. We learned that anger can manifest itself in two very different ways.

One way a depressed person may deal with anger is to turn it inside. This person gets really angry but no one ever knows it. People who internalize anger literally get sick. They often have stomach problems. They may have ulcers or colitis. They also get sick mentally. They stuff all their angry feelings down deep in their souls. The anger is collected and contained and saved for year and years.

Another way depressed people deal with anger is by directing it outside of themselves toward other people or events. Everyone knows this kind of anger when they see it. It may show itself by the labels the depressed person uses to describe other people. "My boss is such a jerk." "Look at the way that arrogant S.O.B. drives."

Dan expressed much of his anger by criticizing. "You're a nag! You're always on my back!" "Our kids are such brats I can't stand to be around them." Like many depressed people, he would often fly into a rage over little things that he had distorted into big things. Depressed people may scream about seemingly trivial things like the dry cleaners missing a spot on a jacket or the line at the grocery store being four-people long. To most of us, these things are just insignificant annoyances in day-to-day living. We don't put much of our energy into getting angry about them. For someone who is depressed, little annoyances seem like the end of the world.

I got mad, too, but I usually held my anger within. It was too risky to express my own angry feelings when the environment we lived in was so fragile and potentially hostile. Also, like many people, I grew up believing that to show anger was not acceptable. Living with Dan's depression, I learned to fear anger. Putting anger and depression together is like adding gasoline to a campfire. The depression is the fire, the anger is the gas, and putting them together can cause an explosion.

It is difficult enough to trust someone who is depressed and it is even more difficult to trust them when they are angry. Families never know what to expect. Saying one wrong word in an argument is enough to cause a raging blaze. The blaze may lead to some kind of violent behavior. A family member may be the target of the violence or the depressed person may turn on himself and commit suicide. These risks cause family members to keep their anger under control (so they think) and locked up inside.

In our family, we all paid a price for keeping our anger locked up. It ate away at us every day of our lives. Anger would leak out in little ways that destroyed self-respect and self-esteem. I found myself screaming at the kids for no good reason. Someone at school dropped an extra assignment on my list of past due papers and I found myself in the parking lot falling apart. It was not the one little thing that the kids did or the one extra project that caused the anger; the anger had been building for a long time.

It had built up from the stress of living in a raging inferno at home. To the rest of the world, Dan and I appeared to be totally normal, healthy and happy. At home, we were like battered firefighters trying to keep ahead of the angry blaze. The repressed anger was like a smoldering volcano that erupted suddenly without warning into a rage out of all proportion to the apparent cause.

It isn't unusual for depressed people to use angry outbursts to control other people. Author Harville Hendrix describes an interesting aspect of this in his book, *Getting the Love You Want*. We learn to use anger from the day we are born. As infants we learned that anger controlled people. We cried when we wanted something, whether it was to be fed, changed or just held. If our needs were met, we were happy. If the response was absent or inadequate and we were left feeling abandoned, hungry, wet and unloved, we cried harder and longer and finally someone would come and take care of us.

As adults, some people still resort to that infantile behavior. They get angry and throw a tantrum hoping that someone will provide them with what they want or need.

Unfortunately, what usually works for infants doesn't

work for adults. No one wants to get near, or take care of and nurture an angry adult. Everyone wants to stay away until the anger subsides. Even when the depressed person seems calm and rational, we learn to keep our distance while we try to determine if we can trust that person again or not.

Depressed people use their angry outbursts to try to change other people. It may work for a while but what they have to recognize is that the anger won't make their lives better or make their depression go away. Anger just won't work as a weapon to control family members in the long run.

STRUGGLING WITH CONTROL— NOBODY WINS, EVERYONE LOSES

Many depressed people are obsessed with control. They are afraid that if they are not in complete control, they will go crazy. They try to control everything in their lives. Their emotions and thoughts are in turmoil and exerting control over the things and the other people in their lives allows them to feel a small sense of security. They put so much energy into controlling other people, they never have to look at themselves.

Depressed people may try to control their spouses, family members and friends by using some of the following manipulative behaviors:

– **Isolating the family**, controlling what family members do, whom they talk to and where they go.

– **Intimidation**, using looks, actions, loud gestures, smashing things and destroying possessions to create fear; treating family like servants.

– **Threatening**, making and carrying out threats to hurt family members emotionally or physically; threatening to commit suicide, take the children away, or abandon the family.

– **Emotional abuse**, putting family members down and causing them to feel bad about themselves, name calling, trying to make others think they are crazy, playing mind games.

– **Economic abuse**, keeping spouse from getting or keeping a job; forcing spouse to ask for money, refusing to provide money for household needs, hiding or locking up the family money.

– Using the children as a weapon, trying to make spouse feel guilty about the children; constantly reminding spouse of all the time he or she spends away from home when the children "need their mother/father."

– Physically abusing the family, attempting to control by pushing, shoving, hitting, slapping, choking, pulling hair, punching, kicking, grabbing, twisting arms, tripping, biting, beating or using weapons against the family.

– Silence, using the silent treatment to punish other people.

– Sexual intimidation, using sex as a weapon to punish the spouse.

Depressed persons often overreact. In relationships they can become perfectionists.

When the people around them are not perfect, depressed people feel it reflects badly on themselves. Perfection, of course, is an illusion but depressed people are not clear thinkers. They have a hard time conceptualizing and remembering details. When they do create a plan for the family or themselves, it often is not a very good plan even though they may think it is perfect. Their distorted ideas of perfection do not in any way resemble real life and when the perfect plan falls apart or runs up against an obstacle of some kind, they get more depressed.

Depressed people also may have the perfect plan for a marriage. They may have expectations of a new house and a picket fence and a beautiful happy wife with a home cooked-meal on the table every night or a handsome successful husband bringing home a bigger and bigger paycheck every year and, of course, perfectly-behaved children. The reality is that once the beautiful, happy wife gets the lumber bill for the picket fence, and discovers that the charge cards are topped to the limit, she trades in the home-cooked meal for a second paycheck, and crawls in the door at 5 p.m. every night with a frozen pizza and a six-pack of soda pop. Or perhaps the handsome successful husband gets laid off from his job and the paychecks not only don't get bigger, they stop altogether, and he has to hustle for any job he can find to help make ends meet. Maybe he even starts drinking or staying away from

91

home for longer and longer periods of time.

The perfect life envisioned by the depressed person is not the reality anymore. He or she may still want, and may even expect, the fantasy world but, in the real world, the bills need to get paid.

The depressed person begins to feel out of control and this makes them furious. They attempt to regain control by making rules that are impossible to live with, expecting the family to abide by these unrealistic absolutes.

The clincher in all of this is that even if the family could fulfill the depressed person's every expectation, it would not make him happy. Depressed people set such high standards that no matter how close the family might get to meeting those standards, they never quite make it to the level the depressed person perceives as perfect. Trying to attain impossible goals makes the depressed person more depressed and the family more angry and upset.

Some controlling depressives may say, "Fine. If I can't have it my way, I don't want it at all." They sell the house and divorce the spouse—and get more depressed. The illness not only affects their personal life but also their professional career. They may leave job after job because they can't do it the way they want to do it. They justify their situation with irrational comments, "Why work when it just makes me more depressed?"

The one thing that creates the most control-oriented problems in a marriage is money. With Dan, money and control walked hand-in-hand. His internal life was so out of control that he needed to compensate by trying to control everything around him on the outside. He tried to control me for a long time, and he did a pretty good job of it. He intimidated me and convinced me he was always right. Depressed people are very often convinced that their point of view on an issue is always the correct one. They usually have no respect for anyone else's opinion on a subject.

After living with this situation for years, I decided I had to start making some decisions about my own life. I got a part-time job working 12 hours a week. As I started to assert myself and regain my self-confidence, I decided I wanted to go back to school. Dan was totally against it and came up with every excuse to stop me. He cut off the money to keep me from going back.

I was able to save $20 a week out of each of my paychecks. Finally, I saved enough to pay the $580 tuition. When Dan realized I had already saved the money for school, he was furious. He realized he could not control me and looked at money as security. He seized every dime we had and, from then on, our income became his. He controlled it like a zealot. I would not give up going back to school, so we continued to live in a nightmare of conflict and hostility.

Fear is really the bottom line of control. Dan's fear, deep down, was that if I went off to college, I would develop more outside interests that did not include him or perhaps become involved with another man. He was convinced that once I graduated and had my own paycheck, I would leave him. Like many depressed people, Dan had an extreme fear of being abandoned. This fear led him to try to hold on to and control everything and everyone in the present as well as the future. His thought was, "If I lose control of you, you will leave me."

COMMUNICATION PROBLEMS

Sometimes families perceive a situation to be hopeless not because of any identifiable faults in the other family members but because they have lost the ability to talk to each other. Instead of talking, they bicker. Even though all the members of the family may realize that the escalation of conflict is destroying them, they are so irritated and upset that they cannot reach out with empathy or compassion anymore. Everyone reacts to conflict and the more they react, the worse it gets.

When our family was at this stage in the recovery process, I began to realize how totally inadequate our communication skills really were. We would have one day of peace and three days of war. After each peaceful settlement, I convinced myself that this was our last fight and from now on we would be okay. By the time the next war came around (and it always did), I was totally unprepared for it. Then I would berate myself with questions like, "Why are you so stupid?" "What makes you think you can fix this mess?"

Friends would ask me, "Why do you stay with a man like this? You knew this would happen, it always does."

I can remember many days spent in total frustration because Dan and I could not talk to each other without fighting. What I didn't realize at the time was that a relationship with a depressed person can only be as good as the relationship that person has with himself. If he doesn't know how to love himself, there is no way he can possibly love or communicate with someone else. No matter how hard I tried to avoid conflict, I could not keep the peace with Dan until he learned to like "Dan" again.

Conflicts in depressive marital relationships manifest themselves in many ways including:

– Arguing and venting of hostilities on each other or silence/withdrawal. Depressed people are afraid to examine their own feelings too closely so they yell and walk away or play the "blame" game.

– Escalation of major blow-ups and causing irreparable hurt to family members. Minor problems become major. Any weakness is perceived as all-consuming.

– Marital infidelity. A depressed person who is manic may use sex as a form of self-medication. The more sexual partners they can have, the better they feel.

– Accusing the spouse of infidelity.

– Excessive possessiveness.

– Disagreements over finances.

– Criticism. The depressed person criticizes other family members for their housekeeping, appearance, sexual performance, career choice, earning power, anything that demeans them as a human being. As criticism "habits" increase, cruel comments are spewed out one after another.

Types of conflict will vary depending on the personalities within the family. Conflicts may be 1) sudden and violent; 2) destructive and humiliating; 3) silent and bitter.

The conflicts may occur for no apparent reason. One minute things are fine and the next minute the depressed person is bouncing off the walls.

94

The home becomes a battleground and in the heat of combat, the blame wars begin. Family members attack each other and victimize their loved ones in order to preserve and protect themselves—no matter what the cost.

They become so locked into a cyclical pattern of anger that every interaction is strained, every verbal exchange is emotionally charged and triggers pain. The conflicts leave the family members feeling bruised inside and out with their morale depleted and their self-esteem destroyed.

HEAVY IS THE LONELY HEART

Depressed people can be physically present, embroiled in conflict, and emotionally absent. "The lights are on but no one is home."

When couples are going through the "ending" period, intimacy often erodes. There were times when I felt grateful that I didn't have to have sex with Dan. I didn't have the desire or the energy. Sex without real love and caring is not fulfilling. I always felt as if it was an endurance test. During this time, I did not get any of the emotional highs one normally gets from lovemaking. When I thought about all the terrible things Dan had done to me, I could not feel loving towards him.

Dan was cold and unloving and I felt frozen inside. He was a freezer and I was the frozen entree.

When we did have sex, I had to block it all out just to get through it. I knew he wanted sex to release tension, I did it for the same reasons I did everything else . . . to try to make him happy. Sex had the same result as everything else I tried. It didn't make any difference. He was never happy.

EASY TO BE CRUEL – REVENGE AND REMORSE

After living with this illness for an extended period of time, family members can begin to get "I'll show you!" attitudes. They are tired. They have tried everything they know how to do to make the depressed person "snap out of it." Nothing has worked. They eventually reach the point of desperation. Living with depression is like watching a very sad, very sick, very degrading movie in which all the family members are the leading characters.

Getting through the day becomes harder and harder. The family members begin to feel out of control. Sadness overcomes them and they are distraught much of the time. They feel isolated and frustrated. The frustration leads to crazy thoughts of revenge. They want to hurt the person who is causing all this pain. They want to get even with him. But at the same time they are hating themselves because they also love that person very much.

I could not fix Dan's depression by acting or behaving or talking in a different way. I eventually got tired of trying and as my own anger increased, I began to have thoughts of revenge followed by feelings of remorse.

There were times when I could feel so much despair that I would leave the house and walk the streets of my neighborhood, walking without a plan . . . just trying to escape. There were times when I wished I could curl up and die.

I felt a lot of revenge and remorse about my lost opportunities. During the worst days of the illness, I had neither a voice nor a choice in how I lived my life. Because I had allowed Dan and his illness to control my life and my decisions, I had given up opportunities that I would never have again and I resented it.

It's natural to feel bitterness over all the time lost to the depression that could have been spent in other more positive pursuits and revenge feelings go all the way around in a family. The kids are mad at each other and blame their parents. The parents blame the kids and each other. Everyone is hurting and everyone wants the pain to stop. Acting on their feelings just increases the pain. Revenge is a cruel way to test someone's feelings toward you and, though it may have worked in the past, in the case of severe depression, it will not work now. A depressed person may seek revenge by committing suicide. They will "show you how much you needed them."

TO LEAVE OR NOT TO LEAVE

By the time a family reaches the revenge state, relationships are in shambles around them. This is usually the time when people decide to leave the relationship rather than endure the pain of staying in it any longer. The emotional price they are paying to keep the family together far exceeds any benefits they get from continuing to live with the depressed person.

When the depressed person is a spouse, partners may be able to walk out of the marriage, get a divorce, and establish their own identity. If the depressed person is a child or a sister or a parent or grandparent, the choice to leave may not be an alternative.

There are some situations where leaving the depressed person is not the best solution. Many spouses and family members prefer to stay and try to help their loved one to survive the illness. Families who choose this route, need to be aware that they are in for a lot of hard work to save their family.

To leave or not to leave is a very difficult decision that each person must make for himself or herself. I worried about what other people would think. I thought no one would understand how I could leave Dan when he needed me so much.

I kept wishing someone would rescue me. I wanted to escape, but I did not want to give up a marriage that meant to so much to me. When Dan's behavior got crazy, I would hide the knives and guns and get rid of his truck keys or lock up the garage. I felt as if I needed to be there to protect him from himself.

Some days I felt as if I was living in hell. I know we survived the darkest days because of love and perseverance. As a family, we stood by Dan, fought for him, lied for him and did everything we could in the hope that some day he would want to crawl out of the darkness and start to live again.

97

BURNING OUT

Coping with depression requires major adjustments of physical and emotional energy. The immediate impact of the illness doesn't begin to reflect the enormous drain on family resources and energies required to help a depressed person cope with what could be a long-term problem. Families take on twice the work they had before but have only half the energy to cope with it all.

Living with anger and resentment takes a tremendous amount of energy. I did not realize how much energy I was wasting being angry with Dan and his illness. I knew I was stressed-out, but I blamed it on school, kids and work. I never thought about what the emotional tension was doing to me.

During my last semester of graduate school, I was approaching complete burn-out. I was tired of coping with the physical and emotional overload and I began to self-destruct. I started drinking and taking valium to ease my anxiety. I was destroying myself. At school and at work friends would confront me about my problems. I would tell them:

"If he wasn't depressed, I wouldn't be so unhappy."

"If he felt better and was not so angry I could talk more."

"It's his fault I can't concentrate on anything."

"This damn depression is driving me crazy."

I tried to separate from Dan without leaving him. This in-house separation included separate activities, separate vacations, separate lives within the same household. We had impulsive separations where I would walk out and then return after a short time. Dan became a workaholic. I did anything I could to cope. I began to call friends and confide. Once this pattern of "mutual alienation" became established, it was repeated over and over again. We tried to talk to one another but the anger was so great and our differences so complex that nothing could get resolved.

There were many times I felt like giving up.

10 | Ending

Dan and I finally realized that many of our relationship problems had been magnified and exaggerated by the depression. Once we recognized that and accepted the depression as an illness that was controlling our lives and destroying our family, we had taken the first step out of denial and toward ending the problem.

Facing reality is tough. It takes persistence and perseverance. Many families get caught in the "if only's" trap which just makes things worse. "If only's" provide us with the opportunity to create a fantasy life that will never come true. "If only I had won the lottery, my life would be better." "If only I had married someone else, I would not be in the mess I am in today." Some people are content to live their entire lives wishing on "If only's."

Through therapy, families can end the wishful thinking and begin to live in the present. Yesterday is old news. While there can be a great deal of value in going back and sorting out the pain, the present reality is what it is. For us, it was time to accept the present and begin to deal with the current problems which surrounded our family

ESTIMATING THE DAMAGES

As we began "ending" the nightmare of our dysfunctional situation, we took inventory of what was left of our family, our emotions, our finances, our self-esteem. Our damage report included:
- Loneliness
- Depression in the other family members
- Reduced effectiveness at work
- Destroyed or impaired family finances
- Faded friendships
- Uncomfortable extended family relationships
- Alcohol and other chemical dependencies
- Extreme rigidity, punitive judgmental behaviors
- Non-loving, pessimistic and perfectionistic attitudes
- Inconsistency
- Denial of feelings and reality
- Humiliating, discrediting, degrading communication
- Betrayal
- Broken promises
- Neglect
- Disallowment of feeling

Reconstructing a family after all of this damage may seem impossible but Dan and I were determined to try.

LETTING GO OF ALL WE KNOW

We had to let go of the way we were in order to accept the way we wanted to be. This was a hard process. In the book *Transitions* by William Bridges he talks in terms of growth, endings, confusion, distress and new beginnings. We grow up believing that growth occurs "by leaps and bounds." Nobody ever talked about the "rebounds." None of us expects to "grow" by losing rather than by gaining. It goes against everything we are taught in our society.

100

Part of the ending process involved accepting the idea that many of the things we believed in the past were no longer true or valid. In order to end the pain of the old relationship, we had to rebound—go back—look at the past with a clear eye and begin to heal the old wounds.

This is where Dale, our therapist, was an invaluable guide. A therapist can help families to feel hope, to see the tiny ray of light. They can guide families towards this light, out of the dark cave they have been living in, and into a new beginning. Good therapists are in the "change" business. They help guide families through all of the pain and bring them to a peaceful place they never dreamed existed.

Through therapy, Dan and I started to change many things, from simple things like negative habits to important things like where we lived. Some families may decide to mentally or physically separate from each other for a while. This can sometimes help them re-establish their own identities and create new ways of living. Separating may also help them to figure out who or what is contributing to the depression and who or what is not.

With all of the complex problems centered within the family of a depressed person, it is easy to understand why the first three or four months of therapy are an ordeal. Through the process of sorting through all the different aspects of the illness and trying to figure out who in the family is suffering from what, family members may discover that they are in reality very different from the way they have been defining themselves.

GIVING UP ROLES AND GETTING OFF THE STAGE

Depressed people tend to label everyone including themselves and their family members who, out of love for the depressed person, may have molded themselves to fit the label given to them. Thus, the entire family may have become like actors playing out roles.

Through therapy, families may discover that they don't have to or even want to play these roles anymore. They can get off the stage and start living their own lives and leave the acting job behind. Because their identities have been so tied up in the depression nightmare they have been living, it is natural for families to feel unsure while they are redefining who and what they want to be.

For me, ending became a time of tremendous growth. When I realized that I had a choice in how I lived, it was like being set free from prison. I finally had the chance to leave the pit that I had been in for years. I didn't even know I was in the pit until Dale pointed it out. It's like growing up in a poor rural community without running water or electricity and never knowing you're poor until you take a trip to the city and find out that other people have bathrooms, washing machines, electric lights, and central heating. Until the trip to the city, your perceptions tell you that what you have is all there is.

IN SEARCH OF REALITY

Most personal growth occurs in ways not of our own choosing. Therapy may have been initiated to change the depressed person but family members may find that the biggest benefits come to them. Once they get out of the depression trap, they never want to go back again. Finding a balance through all the awakening experiences resulting from therapy is a real challenge. The first few months are draining emotionally and physically. Every time I walked out of a therapy session, I felt as if I had run a 20-mile footrace. I have never worked so hard in my life. I thought it would be so easy. You just sat down and talked to someone, right?

Dan and I found out real quick that if the therapy was going to work for us, we were going to have to dredge up all the old dirt from the past—bad decisions, family problems, both of our failings, my contributions to Dan's depression, etc., and take a good, hard look at it. This emotional digging was the most difficult experience I have ever been through.

I began to question every decision I had ever made. I discovered I had been making most of my choices based on what would make everybody *but* Kellie happy. I had no idea why I believed other people's truths and accepted them as my own. The confusion made me fear that I was going crazy. After each session, I kept asking Dale, "Am I okay?"

During the early part of the ending process, I felt as if I was sinking. I didn't know what to believe anymore. Through the early months of therapy, I was on automatic pilot, just kind of numb and not totally willing to give up the past. I was walking a fine line between a miserable past and a frightening unknown future.

Dan was going through his own crisis and during this time it really helped us both feel safe just to know that Dale was there for us. We relied on him a lot and there were times when I thought we were getting too dependent on him. I didn't realize until later that, at this point, there was no way we could help ourselves anymore. We were too entangled in too many problems.

While becoming very realistic about our life, we also became disillusioned. It was like being in a state of limbo; I was not sure who I was anymore and I didn't know who Dan was either. We both began to realize that many of the beliefs and values we had built our lives around and that we thought were set in concrete, were really written in the sand. What we had thought was (the only) reality, wasn't. In therapy, our "reality" was fed into a therapeutic blender and all our thoughts were turned upside down. Suddenly we found ourselves in a scary "no man's land."

FLYING SOLO — ENDING

While being in "no man's land" is frightening, ending is not a form of punishment. It is merely the process of burying the dysfunctional relationships and rejoicing at the prospect of creating a new way of life.

Ending means striking out in a new direction and creating a new path towards the future. With the help of a therapist, our family began to chart our own new path, leaving a trail for the others to follow. Being an explorer is frightening; it means taking a risk. Ending our destructive family patterns was like flying a plane through fog with no instruments when we had never even flown before. There was no way to really know where we were are or what was happening to us.

Our therapist acted as the controller in the tower, calmly and carefully giving us instructions on where and how to land our plane. There were times when we felt very disoriented and not sure we were making the right choices. All we wanted to do was land the plane in a better place than the one from where we took off. There were times when we were not sure where that place was. Everything that used to seem important was not important anymore. We felt lost and uncomfortable. Being in this situation was not enjoyable. There was an emptiness and a feeling of loneliness.

In his book, *"Loving Each Other,"* Leo Buscaglia said, "We need to learn to let go as easily as we learn to grasp or we will find our minds empty and our hands full."

Depression had kept our hands full for a long time. This ending period was a time to let go of the pain we had been living with and to fill our minds with new knowledge that would sustain us on our journey into the new beginning.

The biggest and most destructive storm in my life was an unhappy marriage. Depression came like thunder. It was scary for awhile. After Dan and I worked through the ending process, the clouds began to break and the thunder stopped. There was still a lot of rain and some leftover gray skies but at least some of the fear was gone.

Once a family living with depression starts the ending process, every area of their life begins to open up and no part of their relationship is left unchanged.

Section III

CONFUSION AND DISTRESS

11 | Working Through the Changes

THE MAGIC KINGDOM

"Welcome to the Magic Kingdom" the sign said on the freeway. After spending three days in a compact car with two kids and a depressed husband, I needed a little magic in my life. Dan and I had never taken our kids on a real family vacation and we thought that, after living with all the doom and gloom of the past eight years it would be good for us all to visit the happiest place on earth—Disneyland!

It had been a year since Dan's suicide attempt. Since then, we had been in the process of ending many of the disruptive patterns in our lives. Dan seemed to be doing much better. Unfortunately, he had decided to stop taking his antidepressant medication about a week before we left on our trip. His rationale was that the medication was too expensive and we needed the money for our vacation. He had been feeling good, and since we were going on vacation, he thought he

107

wouldn't be under as much stress as he usually was. We had high hopes that the trip would be a chance for us to solidify our relationship and build some strong bonds as a family.

Four hours into the trip I knew that wasn't going to happen. Our small car was loaded to the hilt with the kids' toys and games and all of our luggage. There was no room to move around. The four of us had never before been in such a cramped space for such an extended period of time. Dan was edgy, the kids were fighting in the back seat, and I was falling back into my role of "I'll make everything okay."

We stopped in Provo, Utah, after about eight hours on the road. As soon as we got to a motel, Dan left on the pretext of getting the car's wheels aligned somewhere and he didn't come back for hours.

We spent two more days driving to California. The longer we drove the more tense we became. Dan was stressed-out because of all the money we were spending. The kids were worn out from the traveling and the tension. By the time we got to the entrance of Disneyland none of us were very excited about our vacation anymore.

Dan's depression had come back in full force. His anger and aggressive attitude had returned. He was on the slide back into a major depressive episode and there was nothing I could do to stop it. By the time we got to the Disneyland Hotel we were no longer speaking to each other. Dan went berserk when I tipped the doorman who brought our bags to the room. The kids were crying, Dan was yelling and I had had it. I went out on the balcony of our room that overlooked the Magic Kingdom and screamed "I can't take it anymore."

Disneyland was a symbol. Perhaps, in the back of my mind, I hoped that something would happen on this visit to the kingdom of make-believe that would cause Dan's depression to magically disappear. Then *our* family could become a happy, well-adjusted family just like the Brady Bunch.

But the "magic" didn't work. It was clear Dan wasn't well yet and neither were the rest of us. No matter how hard we tried we could not wish ourselves well or rush the recovery process.

When we returned home later that week and, during our

therapy session, began to process what had happened on the trip, Dale listened intently and then said, "Welcome to the C/D-Zone."

What is he talking about? I thought.

"Confusion and Distress, the roughest part of therapy," he said. "There are two rules you need to live by during this stage of recovery; number one, don't sweat the small stuff and number two, it's all small stuff."

PERIOD OF TRANSITION

"Confusion and Distress" is a period of transition in which families are trying to let go of the pain and negative patterns of the past while struggling to learn new ways to live in the future. Strange as it may seem, one of the first signs that the family has come through the "ending" part of the healing process and is entering into the next stage is when the depressed person says, "I don't want to be on this medication anymore. I am doing much better and I don't think I need it." Every family that has lived with depression has heard this statement.

Dan had dumped a lot of his emotional garbage in Dale's office during the "ending" process. Also, the medication was taking effect and he was feeling much better. He decided he was cured.

Like many other people who suffer from depression, Dan quickly found out that the feeling of contentment at this stage does not last very long without medication. When he stopped taking his medication he went back to his old behaviors and our life fell apart again. Old problems surfaced again and Dan had a hard time accepting the fact that his depression had come back.

It is not uncommon for depressed people to want to go off their medication as they begin to feel better. However, this is something they should *not* do. If they decide to go off medication, it may be just a matter of time until they begin the downward slide back into depression. It may take weeks or just a few days, but most depressed people will have a major relapse. In the meantime, the family members are left holding their breath and watching the dream of a better life fade back into the old nightmare they thought they had left behind.

Dan's depression returned and he hit bottom again. Then, he agreed to get back on the medication and, once again, begin the long, hard climb out of the pit of despair and despondency. It was much harder the second time because we finally realized there were some tough issues that had to be addressed. Getting rid of the depression was not going to be as easy as we thought.

We spent the next six months struggling through our interpersonal problems.

SCARY HORIZONS – GUSHING TEARS

As we peeled away the layers of pain that had held us so tightly for so long, we did a tremendous amount of grieving. Dale gave us "permission" to grieve our losses and fill the voids in our lives. He helped us sort out significant major problems and conflict areas and he helped Dan mend relationships with family members and the other people in his life. There was a great outpouring of tears because we were finally able to let go of much of the pain we had been holding inside for years.

This was a rough time for our family. It was tough on Dale, too, because he was trying to keep all of us motivated while we sorted through our pain. He was also keeping an eye on Dan, monitoring the medications and evaluating the progress of the treatment.

There were many times when we all felt overwhelmed. We had to concentrate all our energy and keep the focus on our end goals. It was interesting that, with all of the problems we were working through, it was sometimes the routine sessions in therapy when none of us seemed to have anything really important to talk about that produced the most insight. Dale explained to us that this happens because the clients are focusing on the *process* of change rather than allowing themselves to be distracted by the upsetting behavior of the depressed person or other disruptive events in their lives.

Although we had begun our therapy as a result of Dan's attempted suicide, we soon learned that the real issues we had to deal with were the ones that led up to that suicide attempt. Some of these issues were deep, tightly-held beliefs and values that we had been holding onto for a long time.

HOLDING ON

During this period, it is important for families to keep a handle on their feelings and express them in a safe place and at appropriate times. Sometimes, when people are in crisis, their tendency is to unload their feelings on whoever will listen including the depressed family member. This is not a good idea. Using the depressed person as a sounding board rarely helps anyone and may result in even greater strain on the family relationships. Carefully picking the right time and the appropriate person to hear those feelings insures better results.

This is a time when families need to allow themselves time and space to deal with pain and sort out problems. It is important for them to experience all their own feelings, positive and negative. The process is not a linear one. At times it may seem to be a jumbled mess. This is to be expected.

Working through all of these feelings is an intense process. Sometimes family members may feel as if they are going crazy. They may be unable to eat or concentrate on work or sleep.

While I felt encouraged about the fact that Dan was finally acting and feeling better, I had no stable goals or commitments of my own towards which I could direct my activities and I sometimes exhibited uncoordinated and almost frenetic behavior.

Sticking with therapy during the confusion and distress phase of the healing process may be harder than starting therapy ever was. Anyone who has ever tried to make a substantial change in his life knows how difficult it is to accomplish. It is enormously hard work. It is very rewarding but it can also be very draining. While we may truly want to make the changes, we are not always willing to undergo the pain involved in the process of unraveling the specific causes for the depression. There is no telling what old skeletons we

111

might find once we start rummaging around in our emotional closets.

Therapy at this stage can be a very painful process. It's like having your appendix out. You have an ache that won't quit and you look forward to the end of the pain but you also dread going under the knife. This is a definite change from the way therapy was in the "ending" process. You start therapy to end the pain and it usually helps you feel better right away. You feel centered and on target, you have a lot to discuss and it feels really productive. But as the therapy proceeds, you begin to look more closely at internal problems as you venture into what might turn out to be some very difficult territory. Past events that you would rather forget are brought in full view and it can be overwhelming and scary.

Emotional pain is like any other pain. When we feel it we try to protect ourselves from it.

There were times when I wanted to quit because I was afraid I had lost control of my inner being. The therapy was stirring up all the compartments of my life. It hurt too much to go back and look at all that pain.

I didn't know what the future was going to be like. I just wanted to survive. I was sure no one would like me if the therapy made me become someone different from who I was. There were times when I wanted to just stop, forget about all the work I had done, and go back to the way I was before. There were days when I had to literally drag myself to therapy. I looked drained, wore sloppy clothes, used little makeup. All my enthusiasm had been sucked out of my body.

I was afraid to tell my feelings or even to try to find them. I was very scared.

RESISTING CONTROL

Because Dan had been using money as a vehicle of control, especially with me, we attempted to address that problem in our therapy sessions. We set up a contract where I would have a certain amount of money each month for a household account. I felt liberated until I realized that Dan was still attempting to control me by demanding an exact accounting of how every last dime of that money was spent.

I resisted this control by going out and getting a part-time job. Not only did my job provide me with a paycheck, it also gave me a sense of confidence and accomplishment. Because Dan felt threatened by my new-found joy in my job, he attempted to maintain control by resorting to angry outbursts and criticisms about things that did not matter. He told me I was a lousy mother to make me feel guilty so that I would quit my job and stay home. He said I would never amount to anything. I had to listen to hours of his tirades about what I should be doing and how I should be doing it.

When the anger and the criticism didn't work, he threatened to abandon me. He'd say, "Well, have it your way, but I am not going to be around to pick up the pieces when you fall apart!"

He would ignore me, leave the house without saying goodbye and not call from work. He did whatever he could think of to let me know he would not be there for me.

When Dan could not tolerate my being able to function without him, he would reverse his direction (finally) and try to woo me back into dependency by using sex, money, whatever it took, to sweeten the bait so that I would come back into his controlling web.

It was very hard but I learned not to give in. I continued to handle my job, my school assignments, and my children with increasing success. When I hit a rough spot I went to Dale for a much-needed consultation. Dan's need to control was his way to cope and survive his illness. When I held my own, refusing to play the game anymore, he was forced to give it up.

DEALING WITH FEAR

It's frightening to live with uprooted and potentially violent emotions but I learned that the best cure for fear is to attack it and walk right through it. If I ran from my fears, they always chased after me. I learned that it was okay to admit I was afraid. I then had to decide what I was going to do about it?

113

It's difficult to stand up to fear but I began to set some boundaries on what kind of behaviors I would and would not tolerate. Dan needed to know what these boundaries were and I needed to take appropriate action if they were violated.

It's easy for loved ones to blame themselves for the depressed person's misconduct. "If I hadn't said this or if I hadn't done that, then he wouldn't have hit me." This kind of thinking is illogical. The violence is the violator's fault.

If a spouse or other family member is being abused, the first step in the change process is to stop making excuses for the abuser. Family members do not deserve to be beaten up. They may have been part of, or even initiated, a conflict with the depressed person but they do not deserve to get hit.

One fear that families live with on a daily basis is the fear of the depressed person committing suicide. It is a legitimate fear because there is probably a greater chance of someone committing suicide during the confusion and distress stage of the recovery process than at any other time.

The depressed person may be feeling much stronger at this point and actually in a position to do a great deal of damage to themselves and to other people. He has begun to crawl out of the "pit" of depression and no longer feels so helpless. He also has the energy he may never have had before and is now actually able to carry it out.

I was really afraid that Dan would kill himself. Dale and I talked about this at great length in therapy. "If he does, it is something that you have no control over," he told me.

Depressed people make lots of empty promises. They may promise that whatever happened in the past will never happen again. As much as you would like to believe them, you need to take care of yourself first and believe their promises later.

Because of the potential threat of suicide, Dale and I devised a plan that could be put into action quickly in case my worst fears came true. I set aside enough extra money for a hotel room in case I needed to get away. I wrote down the telephone numbers for the police, the local mental health association, the crisis hotline and other appropriate community agencies. I knew where I could go and who I could

114

call on for help if I needed it.

Fear can be paralyzing or it can lead into the process of becoming more self-sufficient. Facing fears may be the motivation that someone needs to become his or her own person. When the spouse and family members reach a point where they can handle their own lives on their own terms, they are much better able to come to terms with the fears associated with their loved one's depression.

Once people learn to count on themselves and not to depend upon others, particularly other family members who are unstable, they have fewer expectations and, thus, are much less vulnerable to being hurt. The less they are hurt, the less fearful they are. When families are able to make their own choices, they are free to walk through life without being immobilized by their fear.

COPING WITH ANGER

Anger, another old spook, is difficult to work through. Family members may have been holding anger in check for a very long time. They may be reluctant to express how they really feel because of the risk of sending the depressed person into another dangerous tirade.

In the past when I argued with Dan, most of the time I was arguing with the illness. There is no reasoning with someone who is depressed. Dan's depression, negative thoughts, and distorted thinking were caused in part by a chemical imbalance in the brain. These chemicals are not capable of rational thinking. I was very careful not to berate and belittle Dan because of the potential that I might be exposing myself to violence. Dan's self-esteem was very low. By continually harping at him, I just added fuel to the banked fire that could flare up at any time.

And yet, I was really very angry at Dan. The anger had been building for years and I had to get rid of it in a way that was not harmful to me or anyone else. This was difficult to do. I spent many hours walking—well, maybe more like marching—around my neighborhood. One day, after a heated argument with Dan, I pulled all the paneling off the family

115

room walls and painted the entire room in about three hours. By the time the job was done I had physically worked off some of the anger and, as a side benefit, the house looked a lot better.

Writing about anger is another way to deal with it. I wrote pages and pages of notes and letters to Dan about all of the rage I had inside. I wrote my feelings in the most graphic words I could find.

During both the "ending" stage and and the "confusion and distress" stage I wrote in a notebook every day. Writing about it and drawing pictures helped me release a lot of my emotion. Once the anger was out on the paper I was better able to cope. When I wrote Dan letters—which I never gave him—I wrote things like, "Why did you do this? Do you think this is right? Did you ever think that the things you did might hurt me? Do you have any idea what this illness is doing to us?" Writing for me was a great vent for my rage.

Anger never comes at the perfect time. Dan and I would get into an argument usually just shortly before we went to bed. I would toss and turn becoming more and more furious with him. Finally, I would get up and do something productive with the anger. Usually, since I was at home, I would clean house or do some other domestic chore. Dishes can be washed in the morning or at night. I decided that, if I was going to spend the night walking the floor so that I was too tired to do housework the next day, I might as well put all that pent-up energy to work. Living with depression is not living in a normal situation, so you have to be flexible and adapt your life as you need to.

Anger comes from living in chaos. Even after months of therapy, a depressed person may continue to act depressed and not be able to handle anything. Depressed people have their good days and their bad days. Families who expect too much from them are in for a lot of disappointment. If the family members can deal with their own frustration and anger while it is still manageable, they are a step ahead of the game.

The confusion and distress stage is an extremely difficult time for the family. The therapist has given "permission" to the family to get angry and everyone is mad at each other in one way or another. In the past, they may never have had, or felt as if they never had, an opportunity to express anger. There may have been one family member who moderated the anger in the past but now everyone is faced with the reality that no one in the house is going to mediate or play referee.

Dale's goal in therapy at this point was to help us reframe our anger and deal with it in more constructive ways than we had done in the past. Once we could truly accept the depression as an illness, we could then begin to redirect our anger towards the situation and away from the depressed person and/or each other.

NO MORE COVERING UP

As our family behaviors began to change through therapy, we became uncomfortable about covering up for Dan's depression. The children and I began to have more respect for ourselves and were no longer willing to conceal the truth. We began to live in a state of truth because it was right for us.

The old spooks of revenge, remorse and self-pity, who cause great havoc for families living with depression, started acting up during the confusion and distress period. About midway through it all, I was really feeling sorry for myself. I resented having to live in the middle of so much pain for no good reason. I had a severe attack of the "poor me's" and the "why me's." Why did I have to suffer through all of this? Look what I have to put up with!

I allowed myself to get pretty depressed over what had happened (remember, the illness is contagious) but then I began to set certain limits on how far down I would let myself go. I allowed myself to get in touch with my feelings of remorse and self-pity, but dealt with them without getting into the revenge state of mind. I allowed myself to feel bad but I accepted that I was not going to destroy myself over it.

My feelings were very real and appropriate; acknowledging them helped me to resolve them. It wasn't until I got a glimpse of how good things could be that I realized how dysfunctional our family life had been.

12 | Shifts in Relationships

WHO IS THAT MASKED MAN?

Living with depression is like being a kid at Halloween. When we were little we believed in the illusion of ghosts and goblins. We were quite surprised when those characters removed their masks and became ordinary people again. We were afraid to trust them, because we were never quite sure when the monster would come out again and scare us to death.

In real life we all wear some masks. They may be invisible but we use them to help keep us safe and protect us from being hurt. We may have a happy mask we put on when we see someone we know that we are trying to impress, we may have a professional mask that we don before we get to work each day.

Depression creates a very real mask and when the depressed person starts to get better and begins to lose the hellish mask he has been wearing, it can be a little unsettling for everyone in the family. In Dan's case, when he began to remove the mask, our kids and I saw a happy face that we had not seen before. We did not quite trust this new face because we were not convinced it was going to stay in place. In a strange way we almost felt let down by Dan's new happiness. We just couldn't accept that it was real. We thought we knew who we were living with and now all that was changing.

When we began to change old patterns we unknowingly set the groundwork for a mighty war.

SHIFTING CONTROL

In our old depression-ruled relationship everyone in the family was tied together, bound by the ropes of the illness. As our recovery progressed, control within the family relationship began to shift. Dan felt anxious and afraid when I began to develop my own strengths. I wanted more say in how I handled my own life.

The fact that I was becoming a new person was very threatening to Dan. While I was progressing he began to regress. His depressive behaviors began to escalate again and he tried to pull me back into what had once been a comfortable life for him. He attempted to intimidate me by moping around, pouting, sulking, or having temper tantrums and acting suicidal. He tried anything that would allow him to maintain control over me.

Our family communication again became very strained. Dan continually misinterpreted what I said and would respond in inappropriate ways. I had to remind myself constantly that it was not Dan who was talking . . . it was the illness.

I knew he truly regretted his actions. He would often leave notes on the kitchen counter apologizing for his behavior. He wrote, "Kellie, I feel really bad about what I said. Sometimes I react and say things because I feel so bad. I am really tired of hurting you . . . I don't know what is going to happen."

The notes assured me that at least he knew his behavior was destructive but he just did not have the ability to stop it.

SAYING GOODBYE TO THE PERFECTS

Slowly, we began to accept the idea that we were not now or ever going to be the perfect family. In fact, there was no such thing as a perfect family. It was time to say goodbye to "The Perfects."

It was at this point that our relationship began another shift into a more positive mode and a new shape. We got serious about stabilizing where we were and we set some specific goals for the future. We took a long, hard look at what we both really wanted and needed from a relationship. We determined what was realistic to achieve and what was not. We stopped being self-destructive and learned how to become strong within ourselves, and the depression once again began to subside. All of the time and energy that we had spent worrying in the ending stage were now used towards a more productive purpose.

TAKING RESPONSIBILITY FOR OURSELVES

Setting boundaries was another issue we addressed in this stage of recovery. The rest of the family needed to know where Dan ended and each of us began. We learned to sort out whose problems were whose and how to avoid taking on each other's junk.

If Dan refused to take his medication, that was his decision.

If I felt abandoned and abused, that was my problem.

If Dan did not approve of my new job, that was his problem, etc.

Setting these kinds of boundaries is important because we really have no control over how other people feel or act unless it comes within the purview of the law. If a depressed person sits and pouts or throws a temper tantrum in an attempt to maintain control, that is his problem. If a family member allows his or her life to be controlled by threats of suicide, that family member has a problem.

Sometimes what seems to be a positive change, turns out to be not so positive. When the attention of the family begins to shift towards something other than the illness and the depressed person's needs, he or she may fall back into depression. The more the family members begin to step away from accepting any responsibility for the depression, the angrier the depressed person may get. It is common for them to want someone to blame for their problems and to want someone to take the heat for solving those problems.

Family members may back down at this point, accept what the depressed person says as truth and go back to the same dark hole they crawled out of during the ending process.

I did this a lot. When friends or family members would ask me why I let myself get sucked back into Dan's depression again, I'd use my old victim reply, "He needs me to take care of him."

As Dale observed these ups and downs, he would confront me about them in therapy. "What do you get out of all of this? Why are you content to go back? Are you ready to face Dan's depression again?" Sometimes therapists ask tough questions. Most of the time I didn't want to know the answers to the questions Dale was asking.

A BREAK IN THE CLOUDS

It was a red-letter day for me when I decided to get out of the victim role I was stuck in and begin taking responsibility for myself and for my own life.

Through much of the confusion and distress period, I felt as though I was living in a prison—both internally and in my external environment. Dan and I had purchased a house that was terribly dismal. At the time we bought it, my frame of mind was pretty dreary and I didn't much care. The longer I lived in that house, the more it reminded me of Dan's depression. The woodwork was a blackish-brown color. The kitchen cabinets were the same color. The appliances and counter tops were a dark, avocado green. I hated that kitchen. Every time I walked in there I felt depressed.

One night a pipe broke and water gushed into the kitchen and damaged the floor. At first, I was horrified, but then I decided it could be a wonderful blessing. Our insurance paid to have the floor replaced. I talked to Dan about replacing the counter tops and wallpapering the kitchen in a light floral design. He said that would be fine with him.

Unfortunately, one of the frustrating things about Dan's depression was that he never said what he meant or meant what he said. The day the workmen showed up, Dan came home to find them in the kitchen and went berserk. He yelled at them telling them they had no right to be in his house tearing it up. He said no one had told him that this was going to happen and eventually he kicked them out. Enter Kellie to patch up the mess and pick up the pieces again.

Unhappy as it was, this was liberation day for me. Because of Dan's irrational outburst, I finally realized that until his illness was under control, I would have to be in command of my own ship and could not expect him to handle anything.

KILLING HIM SOFTLY

Out of what I thought was love I became a super wife, determined to create the best life possible for my family. After six months of dragging in the door after work and preparing a five-course meal, I realized that it's hard to be super-anybody for very long. I also learned that too much care suffocates a depressed person, both mentally and physically, and makes him even more depressed.

Family members cannot save the depressed person from himself or from the illness. Dan had to begin to face the consequences of his actions. Because I was so efficient at picking up and taking care of things and doing everything for him, there was little motivation for him to get well. He relished the attention he got with his illness. When he would feel overwhelmed, he would hang his problems on me. I was just like a coat rack; coat racks hold coats and I held problems. Dan knew he could count on me to take care of any problems for him.

During one of our therapy sessions, I started telling Dale about all of this. He turned around and told me in no uncertain terms, "The caretaking has got to stop! You are slowly and softly killing Dan by taking over all of his responsibilities. You cannot go on like this. If you continue to take care of him, you will kill him. He needs to feel the results of his choices and he needs to understand the consequences of his actions."

I did not want to hear that.

GIVING A MIRACLE A CHANCE TO HAPPEN

Letting Dan take care of himself was really scary for me but I knew Dale was right. The caretaking did have to stop. As hard as it is to let depressed people take care of themselves, it is the only way they will ever have an opportunity to get better. Becoming a martyr for someone is rarely appreciated. It was much healthier for me to become an exciting and dynamic person in my own right and on my own terms rather than to continue complaining about carrying the load for Dan.

Empathy was a much better expression of my concern than the sympathy I had been expressing in the past. Empathy appreciates the difficult situations that the illness has caused for the depressed person but allows him the space to solve his own problems.

Depression with all of its negative aspects did one very positive thing for Dan and me. It allowed us the opportunity to start over. It was like a wake-up call, a signal that things were not working right and it was time to start over and figure out new ways to live. Through therapy, our family learned new ways of handling the old spooks and goblins that had been ripping our lives apart.

13 | Sex and Intimacy

FOR BETTER OR WORSE

Some depressed adults have no interest in nor do they get any pleasure from sex. Their self-esteem is so low, they can't understand why anyone would want to make love to them. Sex to them is just one more obligation, one more demand, and one more overwhelming task. They are afraid of not being able to perform or to respond adequately. By abstaining from sex, they eliminate the risks of failure or rejection. This dysfunction can seriously affect their marriage.

On the few occasions when Dan and I did make love, he was so desperate to get any "high" possible, he used sex as a way of self-fulfillment. Afterwards, he had no energy left to try to please me or meet my needs and he resented having to make love. His only intention was to achieve release as fast as possible with as little effort as necessary.

Unfortunately, it is the spouse who pays the price for the depressed person's pain. He or she is the one who is left unfulfilled and feeling unwanted.

During the confusion and distress period, poor sexual performance becomes the scapegoat for other interpersonal problems that couples just don't have the energy to face. I thought all our problems would be solved if Dan and I could just get close and make love once in a while. But sex does not solve the problems resulting from accumulated anger and resentment.

TRYING AGAIN

Once Dan's medications began to work and the therapy started shining some light into our relationship, the warmth began to build and the desire for sex, at least on Dan's part, began to increase. Unfortunately, there were still a lot of mixed messages being sent and, for me, sex at this point still was less than satisfactory.

In the past, one the main features of Dan's depression was his lack of interest in sex. Now, he was beginning to desire sex on a regular basis but I did not yet share his warm feelings. I felt used and abused. I had tried for months to get him to show some interest in sex to the point where I doubted that all the aphrodisiacs in the world could improve our love life. I was discouraged with the whole sexual experience.

By now, however, I had begun to realize that I was in control of what happened to me and that I didn't have to participate in any sexual activities if I didn't feel comfortable about it.

Dan and I had had a satisfying and loving sex life before the depression so the process of picking up the pieces of this part of our relationship was not as difficult as it might have been. For couples who have had an unsatisfying sexual relationship in the past, it will be difficult at first, to establish a good relationship that they have never really had. It may be, quite literally, like making love for the first time because neither the depressed person nor the well partner are the same persons they once were.

Some partners are repulsed by the depressed person, remembering the way they've been treated in the past. They may feel as if they are degrading themselves by submitting to sex. These people need to take it slowly and work through their feelings as they attempt to rebuild their sexual relationship.

All couples coping with depression need time to work through their feelings about their sexual relationship. Each of them needs to realize the importance of talking about why they are not ready to participate in sexual activities just yet. The subject should be approached without blaming and by saying in a matter-of-fact way something like, "This just does not feel right to me. I am having a hard time relating to you on such an intimate level because I feel badly about the way things have been between us and I need some time to heal."

MIXED EMOTIONS

Like everything else in depression-laden relationships, feelings are not going to be consistent throughout the recovery process. Both partners may become very angry and upset over all this inconsistency. This is understandable because they are giving so much of themselves to rebuild their relationship. Creating intimacy is hard work. If well partners sense any kind of rejection whatsoever (real or imagined), they may start to scramble to find a safe place for themselves so they won't get hurt. They may start questioning, "Does my partner really love me? If she does, why is she rejecting me?"

As the therapy went on, and the recovery progressed, Dan and I began to work these issues out. Once we had worked through some of our pain, we still had some ups and downs to get through. For a few weeks, we went on a real high, sexually, but this didn't last. I would feel comfortable making love one week, and the next week something would happen to remind me of the way it used to be and our seemingly improving sex life would fall apart again.

Romance goes out the bedroom door when depression walks in. For the well partner, it can be confusing trying to figure out who it is walking back into the bedroom and climbing into the bed. Is it the depressed person or the new recovered person?

It was really hard for me sometimes to figure out who

Dan was at any given moment. After awhile I decided to stop wondering and just ask him who he was before we got in bed. If he was showing signs of being depressed, I knew better than to push for romance because to push would have made it worse than to have nothing at all.

It was very discouraging at this point because I thought it would never get better. But it did. Once we began to work through the relationship issues, sex became what it was meant to be, a loving and sharing time that was gratifying for both of us. We each began to get our own needs met and sex became a loving condition of a healthy relationship, not a weapon or a way to mend conflicts.

14 | Kids and Chaos

"We cannot tell our children the fairy tales that we were told."

> *"no one else*
> *is to know all this but us; even love will*
> *not initiate the outsiders;*
> *it is a closed club,*
> *speaks a secret language,*
> *the password less than a flicker of the eyelid,*
> *knowing, impenetrable, beyond influence."*
>
> -Kathleen Cushman
> "Brothers and Sisters"

DEPRESSION AND CHILDREN

Raising children in an environment in which someone is suffering from depression is like trying to raise kittens in a kennel with a pack of dogs lunging at them from all sides. When a parent is depressed, the kids usually suffer from after-effects, the fallout of depression.

A depressed mom is a mom who cannot give adequate care to her children. She may constantly ridicule and berate her children. She may blame them for her depression. In her depressed state of mind the kids are just another headache. Just talking to them may be a major chore. She may not want to talk to anyone, let alone a three-year-old who (in her mind) has spent the entire day tearing the house apart.

A depressed dad may withdraw and spend no time communicating or sharing with his children. He may yell at them and criticize them constantly for what they have or have not done.

Parents involved in depression may wonder why their children cannot project a positive attitude. They don't realize that they never talk to their children or communicate in positive ways with them. This lack of attention hampers the child's attempts to develop social skills. Living with depression may, in fact, stunt the emotional, social and cognitive growth of children.

For kids living in this type of environment, it's life on the ragged edge all the time. They don't know what the family standards are because they are usually unspoken and often change constantly.

While many children who live in healthy families look forward to seeing their parents at the end of a busy day, kids who live with a depressed parent are stressed at the arrival of the parent. They know that from the minute their parents walk in the door, verbal abuse may begin. Children hear things like:

"You never do anything right."

"All you do is cost me money."

"I am tired of you ruining everything."

"You are the reason why we never get to do anything."

"If you would try harder you would not have these problems."

Children who live with the fallout of depression usually have self-esteem problems. They may resist sharing, clam up and hold all of their feelings inside. They may use drugs as a means of escape. They may become the problem children at school because they need attention so badly.

NO SHELTER FROM THE STORM

If depression is causing one or both of the parents to withdraw, the children soon begin to show signs of neglect. Neglectful parents provide no shelter from life's storms for children. They may be physically in the house with the children but because they are so depressed, or caught up in the depression, they may have no emotional capacity to give much-needed love and attention to their children. They can appear to be uncaring and seem to see their children only as an obligation. In their eyes, there is no joy to be gained from having children.

Neglected children feel that they are not worthy of anything or anyone. They may have little motivation to do well in school and may feel why try since no one cares about them anyway.

Children who live with this family illness for long periods of time accept the actions and reactions of their depressed parents as normal. They assume that all parents are just like their own. Eventually, these children come to understand that their family has a shared secret that no one dares to reveal. To everyone else, the family living with depression may present a picture of idyllic bliss but for the kids in that family, life is a much different story.

Inside the dark house of depression there may be rigid rules. In her book *It Will Never Happen To Me,* Claudia Black writes about growing up in an alcoholic family and the rules she had to live by:

> Don't talk.
> Don't feel.
> Don't trust.

These same rules usually apply for children who live with depression.

LABELS THAT STICK

In dysfunctional families impacted by depression, like those affected by alcohol abuse, the individual family members often play certain roles. The roles we are given as children tend to be the roles that we carry with us throughout our lives. A child in a dysfunctional family may be labeled "good" or "bad" or "smart" or "stupid." One child may assume the role of the "caretaker" of the family. This child is super-responsible and becomes almost a third parent to the rest of the children. These "mini-parent" children are usually the cornerstones of their families. They are the glue that holds the whole shaky house of cards together. They are often seen by the relatives and others as "perfect" children when, in fact, their tremendous achievements on behalf of the family are masking their own insecurities and low self-esteem.

Another role that some children in dysfunctional households play is that of "trouble causer." These children are always in trouble. They act on impulse and are very defiant. Their role in life is to take the focus off of Dad or Mom's depression. These kids absorb much of the anger and frustration that is lurking within the family system. While they seem like tough and unlovable children, inside they are very scared and lonely. They sub-consciously believe they really are trouble-causers and deserve to get everything in the way of anger and hostility that comes their way.

The "wandering" child is a child who gets lost in the shuffle. These children are quiet and rarely seen or heard. They lack a sense of identity and don't request or get much attention in their lives. They are not willing to risk any kind of bad behavior and, consequently, go through their childhood feeling unimportant and unloved.

The "family comedian" is another role in which the child diverts attention from the illness to himself by acting silly. Acting funny works great for these children until they can no longer hide the pain of living with depression or alcoholism. They usually are absolutely terrified about what is happening in their world.

The "unscathed" child doesn't fit in any of the above roles. These children somehow escape most of the effects of depression. They may have grown up before the depression became severe or they may have benefitted from the influence of grandparents and other extended family members who helped fill in the nurturing gaps that were missing in the immediate family system.

No matter what the family roles are, they all arise out of one central fear, the fear of confrontation. All of these roles allow children to somehow avoid confronting anyone. The "caretaker," for example, smooths things over to avoid confrontations; the "wanderer" avoids confrontation by becoming invisible.

LET'S PRETEND WE'RE NORMAL

In addition to the rules and the roles, there are lots of secrets in a depressed family. Everything is taken very seriously. There is no "unity" within the family and any conflicts that come up are ignored, denied or blown out of proportion. Children are isolated and left alone much of the time. They have no rights to privacy or anything else.

Even though all of this is going on, the children are commanded non-verbally to play a "let's pretend we're normal game." Normal families usually have one or possibly two parents who run the household. In a family in which one parent is depressed, there is usually no one in charge. If Dad is depressed, Mom is so busy worrying about him that she is mentally and, perhaps physically, unavailable to her children. Dad can't parent the kids because emotionally he does not have it to give. So the parents sometimes resort to controlling their children by abusing them or threatening them with violence. Children whose parents suffer from depression don't feel secure or safe anywhere.

CHILDREN AS CO-DEPENDENTS

Children can become over-responsible, acting like small adults. A typical night for a "caretaker" child as young as eight years old might include: babysitting siblings, cooking dinner, cleaning up the mess, doing his/her homework and getting everyone in bed, just to keep peace in the family. These children miss their childhoods because they have to "parent" their own sick parents.

Children will go to great lengths to do whatever it takes

to preserve the family unit and take care of Mom or Dad or cover for them. Even though, deep inside, children wish that their parent would not be depressed anymore, they sometimes sub-consciously do everything they can to maintain the depression.

They will make excuses for their parent's actions. They tell their teacher that their Mom is out of town and cannot come to the school program when the truth is that Mom is home in bed depressed. They become little enablers.

The more depressed the depressed person becomes, the more the children become obsessed with him or her. The depressed person receives all the attention of the family just as if he or she were a new baby. The children tend to rally around to try to help and become obsessed with how mom/dad is doing.

When children focus all of their attention on a depressed parent, they become co-dependent. They focus totally on the depressed parent's needs and totally ignore their own needs and wants. The problem with this is that children want to please their parents and when they cannot seem to please the depressed parent, they try even harder, which doesn't work either. Then comes the undeserved guilt.

Children living with depression carry tremendous amounts of guilt around with them. They believe that if they would only do things "right," the depressed parent would get better. They believe that if they only try harder the depressed parent will change.

STRATEGIES THAT HELP

Kids in a depressed family need to be nurtured and loved. They are like victims of a war they never started and they need to be comforted and cared for. There are several strategies I read about in a wonderful book, *Marriage on the Rocks,* by Janet Geringer Woititz, that helped my children deal with Dan's depression and alleviated some of the serious and psychological effects the depression had on them. These are some tender treatment concepts that can be followed in a loving and caring manner.

Open the Lines of Communication. With my kids, I had a difficult time telling them the truth about their father's illness. I wanted to protect them from the reality of depression. I thought I was helping them if I kept telling them that everything was okay even when it obviously was not. The kids, on the other hand, knew things were not okay and their imaginations ran wild. They sometimes believed they were the cause of the problem and that if I could not be honest about it with them, about what was happening with their father, then it must be so bad that no one would ever understand it.

Dale helped me see that I needed to change. I learned not to lie about anything and to tell my children the truth.

Once I started opening up to the children, they started thinking about and then talking about their own fears. When I finally got honest and gave them the straight story, they began to trust again.

While talking is important, listening is vital. Listening involves much more than just hearing the words. Children need eye contact and reassurance that they are understood. Good listeners don't judge. Good listeners just listen. It was also vital that I did not ridicule or criticize what my children were telling me. A trusted confidante is not a critic.

We cannot continue to tell our children the fairy tales that we were told about any part of our lives and that includes talking about depression. Children have a wisdom and a way of knowing that defies all adult comprehension.

Keep Confusion to a Minimum. Confusion adds to the chaos that surrounds families living with depression. While working through the change process, we started to take some small steps to organize our lives. Children like consistency. They become overwhelmed by confusion. They like going to school at 8 a.m. and having reading class at 9 a.m., recess at 10 a.m., math at 11 a.m. and lunch at noon. They know what to expect and they perform better knowing what the normal routine is. Creating routines helps eliminate chaos.

Set Some Reasonable Family Rules. Rules are like traffic lines on the freeway; they give children some direction in their lives and provide some boundaries to help them feel safe. Imagine how we, as adults, would feel if someone removed all of the lines painted on the streets. It would be confusing and dangerous and we would feel tense and nervous about driving anywhere.

Be Patient and Understanding. It is important to explain what is going on and why and also to show patience and understanding. If a normally kind and loving parent turns into a raging maniac, the kids need to know why.

Teenagers dealing with a depressed parent may react in a number of different ways. They may fear being shunned by their friends if anyone finds out that Mom is "crazy." They may worry about "catching it" somehow and becoming depressed also. They may become angry, edgy and even depressed themselves. They may need reassurance from professionals.

Family sessions with Dale really helped our children. I checked out books on depression from the public library to help them understand the illness. We helped them to acknowledge their fears and involved them in the recovery process.

Let Them Grow. I stopped making all of the decisions about my children's lives for them when I realized that by doing this, I had been denying them opportunities for growth. I began working with them to define limits that would still allow them plenty of room to grow. I stopped judging their behavior and I stopped keeping score. I let them begin to learn how to live their lives in a self-directed manner.

Admit Your Mistakes. As parents, Dan and I talked with our kids about the mistakes we both had made in dealing with the depression. The kids responded with lots of love and respect.

Don't Make Excuses. I stopped trying to cover up for Dan and stopped making excuses to the children about his behavior. Actions do speak louder than words and my kids, like most kids, watch actions like sharp-eyed little hawks. They knew why their Dad was not at the school program and if I tried to make excuses, it just made the situation worse. I began to tell it like it was. The kids understood and believed me and it earned me their trust for the future.

Don't Use Kids As Go-Betweens. This was one of the dysfunctional traps I fell into. I knew that if I approached Dan about something, the potential was great that he might react negatively. I would send my message with one of the kids because it was unlikely that they would be attacked in quite the same way as I might have been. So, unthinkingly, I used the kids more and more as my communication links with Dan deteriorated. The child then takes all the risk and bears all the potential pain of any confrontation that ensues.

SOME PITFALLS TO AVOID

In addition to the foregoing suggestions, there are some pitfalls to try to avoid for parents raising children in the same household with a depressed person.

Pitfall No. 1: Refusing Help. None of us is born a great parent. We mostly go by what we saw our parents do, and we may read some books, and then hope for the best. Many of us think we can do it all and that we can do it alone. This may work for a time but the day will come when coping with the struggle of both depression and children simply becomes overwhelming. When this happens, don't be reluctant to admit the need for some help. Help can come in many forms: an occasional babysitter, parents, support groups or a personal family therapist. I learned to find the help I needed.

Pitfall No. 2: Creating Crisis Out of Nothing. When I was under stress, I tended to overreact to anything and everything our children would say or do. After so many years of living with depression I got on a track of trying to fix everything and make everything "all better again." When my kids were upset, I wanted to jump in and solve everything for them. I was so afraid the kids would get depressed that I tried as hard as I could to right anything that went wrong and fix everything. I learned to take it easy, slow down and not take the kids' minor problems so seriously. Whenever possible, I let them solve their own problems.

Pitfall No. 3: Becoming Overcommited to the Children. Because I felt neglected by Dan, I tended to overcommit myself to and became totally involved with our children. I knew everything there was to know about those kids and they became like puppets who depended totally on

137

Mom or Dad to pull their strings. It was vital that our kids be allowed some independence to deal with life at certain points. They needed to be able to develop a sense of self-confidence and self-esteem that could carry them through their future lives.

LOVE THEM AND LET THEM GO

Parenthood is a process, just like growing up. There are sequences in the process and all parents are going to make some mistakes but the world won't come to an end. We need to take some time to play with our children, to develop some family traditions. These can be as simple as playing card games together at the kitchen table or making some popcorn and watching a video together.

Children can be great teachers. They can teach us about directness, about spontaneity and about the joy that captures and surrounds special moments that we spend with them. My kids taught me a lot about how to deal with depression and also a great deal about forgiving.

As Robert Fulghum suggests in his book *It Was On Fire When I Lay Down On It:*

"You will never really know what kind of a parent you were or if you did it right or wrong. Never. And you will worry about them as long as you live. But when your children have children and you watch them do what they do, you will have part of the answer."

"Don't worry that they never listen to you; worry that they are always watching you.

"Learn from them. They have much to teach you.

"Love them long and let them go early."

15 | Telling Others

Depression is a disease that reaches far beyond the confines of the immediate family. When someone is ill most people want to rally around and help them get well. Friends and relatives want to do what they can and employers want to have the ill person back on the job. Dealing with all of these people who are trying to understand can be a challenge to the sick person's family.

THE INVISIBLE ILLNESS

Living with depression takes the same toll on families that living with cancer, AIDS, or any other chronic illness does. In some respects, it is worse because it is not so apparent to the rest of the world.

Our close friends and relatives had seen the signs of Dan's depression and had watched our family being torn apart. They didn't know that depression was the cause of the problem but they had been troubled by Dan's disturbing behavior.

There were many times when I lied about why Dan failed to show up at a family gathering or why he was so unresponsive when someone asked him to go somewhere. Before we sought help for the depression, I lied because I didn't want anyone to think bad things about him. I believed that what they thought about him was a direct reflection of what they thought about me.

TELLING THE STORY

Trying to explain the how's and why's of depression sometimes leads to more problems. When I finally told friends and relatives that the reason Dan had been acting the way he had was because he was suffering from depression, it was difficult, if not impossible, for them to accept that it was a mental illness that was causing his problems.

They just could not believe that Dan would not go golfing or to the movies or on a picnic with them because of depression. If, on the other hand, I had told these same friends and relatives that Dan had the flu or cancer or even AIDS, they would have accepted that as a valid reason for his change of behavior.

Depression is an illness that is hard for people to understand. The parents of the depressed person may blame the well spouse and accuse him/her of not being a good husband/wife.

So much heartache could be avoided if others could understand the illness better. Eventually, Dan's withdrawal caused many members of our extended family to get angry and they retaliated by ignoring him.

DEPRESSION IS NOT ON ANYONE'S SOCIAL AGENDA

Depression by its very nature drives people affected by it into isolation. They simply cannot communicate with others in their environment. Our social life went down the drain. This is not surprising. Most people don't understand mental illness and they certainly don't want to have it over for dinner. We stopped being invited to parties. Our friends fell by the wayside. After about a year, most of the friends I had were people I knew from work and school who did not know Dan.

Because friends are uncomfortable being with you, they hesitate to have anything to do with you. We had to accept the fact that any rejection by others is not a personal rejection but a rejection of the illness. People often conveyed a dislike for Dan when it was actually the depression they despised.

SOMETIMES TRYING HARDER
JUST MAKES IT WORSE

It doesn't take long, though, to realize that neither anger nor attempts to bring the depressed person out of his isolation will be successful in alleviating this illness. Just as you cannot cure cancer by taking people to more social events, you cannot cure depression by insisting that depressed persons accept social obligations and interact with other people.

Even so, well-meaning friends and relatives will offer their fair share of solicited or unsolicited advice. There may be a great deal of blaming. What people cannot understand, they sometimes cannot tolerate.

On many occasions, family members and friends would ask me, "How is Dan doing?" I got so tired of hearing that question. I wanted someone once in a while to ask me how I was doing. No one ever did. Of course, I was good at covering up all my pain and, then, I didn't have much time to spend telling anyone about all my problems. I still had to fix dinner, pick up kids from school, do the laundry, work at my job, go to school, clean out the flower boxes, and do all the other household chores.

Because I was the well spouse, I was (or I thought I was) expected to know why Dan was depressed and to take responsibility for every detail of our lives. I was constantly trying to cover all the bases. I felt as if I had to do everything. Dan was resisting paying for his treatment and, because he was maintaining strict control over the family money, I had to become like a snake to make sure we didn't get behind in our bills. I had to slither around and try to find out what our bank balances were, without him knowing I knew. I had to make sure the insurance was paid and that prescription receipts were submitted and kept current. I lived in fear that if I confronted him, he would hide the money and I would never find it. So, I slithered and felt like a slime.

No one can say how high a price you pay with this illness. I felt sorry for myself and for all the other men and women who are forced to cover for their depressed spouses.

As far as other people are concerned, though, the well spouse always takes a back seat to concerns about the depressed person. I just tried to get through one day at a time.

While I was afraid of the depression, it was a nominal fear compared to my greatest fear—that Dan would kill himself. I was so afraid that if he did, people would think it was my fault. I felt that I could not confide anything to anyone, that no one would understand.

SAD DAYS . . . HOLIDAYS

Getting together for family celebrations became extremely difficult. I dreaded going to parties or dinners because I was not sure who Dan was going to offend or how he would offend that person and I knew that I would hear about it for days after.

Many depressed people don't feel like celebrating. They aren't comfortable around happy people and all the joy and festivity in the world will not make them happy. I learned quickly that holidays and family get-togethers at our house were never going to be like the Hallmark cards portray them.

About two years after we were married, Dan told me that we would be buying no more Christmas or birthday presents. He did not give anyone in his family a gift in six years.

On our 10th anniversary, I rented a hotel room and ordered dinner to be brought in. I had spent days planning and I had candles, special music, cards, bubble bath, and all the other extras to make this the most romantic of evenings.

The women in my office knew what I was doing and that it had taken every dime of my paycheck for the previous two months to pay for everything. They all pitched in and bought me new lingerie.

When the night came, I left a key to the room in a card that the babysitter was to give Dan when he got home. The card instructed him to come to the hotel room 774 and that the dress was formal. When he knocked on the door, I couldn't wait to open it.

As soon as I saw Dan, I knew that the whole night was a mistake. He was wearing his greasy work clothes with dirt from head to toe. It was a total contrast to my black-sequined dress and 6-inch high heels. He did not want to take a shower and couldn't believe that I had actually done this. He looked at the cards and decorations and barely smiled. Reluctantly, he stayed and ate dinner and then watched television. I fell asleep. The next morning, Dan left at 7:00 to go fishing with some friends. It was terrible. I felt rejected again. Dan was so involved in his illness that he didn't know or care how he hurt me.

Creating warm and long-lasting friendships is not high on the depressed person's agenda. They don't really have any energy to give to build rational and caring relationships with other people and they tend to demolish them instead. Thus, the holidays and any other special occasions are times when you walk on eggshells and hope for the best.

Accepting that depression might ruin my plans gave me the opportunity to make some choices. I could attend family functions with a strategic plan in place so that, if necessary, I could leave early. Or I could go alone.

LEAVING

When a family member living with depression is asked about how or why they continue to live with such a difficult situation, they tend to say things like, "Oh, it's not that bad all the time, you just caught him/her on a bad day."

That satisfies the others in your life for a while. What they don't know is that every day is a bad day when you are living with someone who is depressed. Our culture seems to idolize the martyrs who stick with a sick person, no matter what. I felt that I should stay with Dan even though he was unloving and uncaring. I told myself that if I were a good person, I would not resent it. And I felt the others in our life would not understand if I chose to leave him.

There are many men and women who get depressed and are hell to live with. They can be mean and abusive. They may refuse to go to counseling or to attend a support group. They blame the doctors when they don't get well. They can be demanding, bitter and hostile.

If you feel as though you cannot live with it anymore, don't fight a losing battle; get out. Eventually, I accepted the fact that I did not need anyone's approval if I did decide that I wanted to leave.

TELLING EMPLOYERS ABOUT THE ILLNESS

In recent years, depression in the workplace has resulted in enormous losses to American companies through absenteeism, lost productivity, and huge benefit claims paid to cover the costs of the treatment of the illness. While employers know something about depression, like friends and family members they also have some preconceived ideas about it.

Chances are good that an employer has watched the depressed person go downhill, and has noticed co-workers covering for him or her. When the depression gets overwhelming no one knows quite what to do about it.

For families, it's hard to know whether or not to tell an employer about the diagnosis of depression. It depends on the situation. There are two things to think carefully about before jumping in and telling all. Is the depression affecting performance at work? Is the employer understanding and not likely to hold the illness against the employee in the future?

Some employers still feel there is a stigma attached to such an illness. Once they are told about the diagnosis, they may constantly be looking for signs of depression to use against the employee. Some employers, however, have been educated in the illness and will encourage an employee to seek treatment and to get the right medication to help his/her concentration and work-related behaviors.

Many large companies have an employee assistance program (EAP) to provide counseling for people who suffer from depression and other mental dysfunctions. The depressed person and his/her family may want to seek help through the employee assistance program first before approaching the employer.

If the depression is severe and requires hospitalization, it is important to tell the employer that the depressed relative is in the hospital being evaluated for an illness and that the employer will be kept informed as information becomes available.

One of the main concerns people have about telling an employer about their depression is how it will affect their insurance coverage and, thus, their ability to pay for treatment. Many group plans have some mental health coverage. If the coverage is available, the employee must then decide whether or not to use it considering the stigma that may be attached to it. Once a claim for mental health care is filed, it is inevitable that some people at work are going to find out about it.

Even when insurance is available for the treatment of depression, the coverage is usually not nearly adequate enough to cover the costs of the illness. This is where depression really begins to take its financial toll. Until the bills start to add up, most families don't realize that, in addition to the human costs, the financial costs of depression can be staggering.

SETTING THINGS STRAIGHT

Dale taught our family some effective strategies that helped us to deal with our friends and relatives.

1. Before I told relatives about the diagnosis, I called the mental health association in my area and got some pamphlets about the illness. It is very helpful to have the support of valid information about depression to give to family members.

2. I made sure I didn't blame anyone for Dan's illness. When people think about depression, they tend to think that "somebody" must have done something to cause or contribute to it. I spent a lot of time reassuring everyone that it was a physical problem and that it was not anybody's fault.

3. I accepted the fact that I would not be able to convince some people that depression was the "real" problem.

4. I came to understand that most people genuinely care but that in trying to help they sometimes do or say things that seem cruel and unjust. People offered to let Dan stay at their house for a few days "to get away from it all" when I felt that I was the one who really needed the break. It doesn't seem fair, and it isn't, that the depressed person seems to get all the sympathy.

5. I learned to be honest. I stopped covering up for the depression. I decided to tell friends the real truth and nothing but the truth. I stopped taking it personally when they appeared not to understand. After all, I was living with the illness and I didn't understand it.

Once I had told our family and friends about Dan's depression, I could begin the process of handling day-to-day communication problems and interpersonal problems that had been and were continuing to be created by the depression.

16 | Turning the Corner

FINDING OURSELVES AGAIN

As Dan and I worked our way through the confusion and distress we had been stuck in, we began to see where we were in terms of creating a new beginning for our family. Through the confusion and distress stage, we became lost enough to find ourselves again. It was exciting to feel in control of our future.

We recognized that each of us is in charge of our own happiness, that we cannot expect anyone else to create happiness for us nor can anyone demand it of us. We gave up the old illusions of the past that we had so badly wanted to believe in and we replaced them with our new hopes and new dreams. We learned not to demand perfection in a world that was not perfect.

We began to take off the masks we had been wearing to hide the pain we had kept buried for years.

Acknowledging all of this is a tough job but it is just the tip of the iceberg and it takes strength and courage to explore

147

the rest of it. It is at this point that many families leave therapy thinking that they are cured.

What these families don't know is that the parts of the iceberg that are under the water will continue to create difficulties and they may find themselves back in a therapist's office again working on old problems that have remained unsolved. Until they work through the layers of ice below the surface of the water, hidden problems will continue to affect the family relationships.

DOING GOOD BUT FEELING BAD

At this point, therapy offers a seemingly lousy bargain; in order to feel better, you get to feel worse for a while. Not only do you get to feel worse, but you get to pay a pretty good sum of your money to a therapist to help you feel worse!

So, why do so many people go through all of this and seek out a new beginning? Because they are motivated by the vision of what they want to become. Motivation separates those who stay in therapy and stick it out through the recovery process from those who leave and continue to feel miserable.

Therapy allowed Dan and me the chance to re-create our lives with the help of a trained professional. It helped us freeze the action for a moment and allowed us an opportunity to examine the destructive patterns that had been destroying our relationship.

Going into therapy did not mean that we were weak, mentally disturbed or emotionally unbalanced. Therapy helped us understand why we thought the way we did, it helped us learn to express our feelings, and it helped us grow and change. As we began to see more clearly, our problems became easier to understand and less intimidating.

Dale stressed to us that during this period we should not create any more change in our lives than was already occurring. He said, "This is not the time to move, get a divorce, change careers or make any other major life-altering changes. This period of therapy requires all of your energy and endurance. These are times when no one in your family is thinking clearly. It's advisable to postpone any major decisions

148

until your family gets in a more stable condition."

Our trip to Disneyland was just one example of how Dan and I wanted to jump right in and change our entire lives immediately. Dale continually reminded us that we were in a state of process. We were sifting through the rubble of the past and while it was okay to experiment with new behaviors, it was not the time to get wild and crazy and make dramatic changes in our personal life. "This time should be used for healing and rejuvenation," he told us

Dale also emphasized that there were no fast cures for depression, that it takes time to assimilate what has happened and even longer to sort out the whys and hows. As much as we would like, human beings are not coffee pots that can be plugged in and expected to produce immediate results. Dan and I needed time to think, to process our thinking, and to work through our problems. Our old relationship was ending. The behavior patterns and illusions that we had been carrying around for years were being stripped away. We were coming to the end of winter but the old rubbish needed to be raked up and cleared away from our inner selves before the spring planting of the seeds of our new selves could begin.

Our feelings were intense but we were learning how to deal with these feelings more appropriately. Through therapy we learned to communicate more effectively. We learned to end our statements to each other with a comma not a period. This technique allowed us to open up to each other's ideas. We began to catch the negative messages we were sending to each other. Dan worked really hard to stop himself before he said something demeaning or rude.

We began working on our conflict management skills. Dale gave us a six-step method for resolving conflicts that has been used in the business world for years.

1. IDENTIFY THE PROBLEM
2. GENERATE A NUMBER OF SOLUTIONS
3. EVALUATE THE ALTERNATIVES
4. DECIDE ON THE BEST SOLUTION
5. IMPLEMENT THE SOLUTION
6. FOLLOW-UP WITH THE SOLUTION

We posted this list of steps on the refrigerator, on the

149

bathroom mirror, in the car, and anywhere else we were likely to see them every day. I quickly memorized those six steps and still use them to this day.

Through the therapy process, our family discovered that many of life's problems eventually can be solved by pure, strong-standing persistence and dedication to the ultimate goal.

ENLIGHTENMENT

The enlightenment and learning that came from working through the confusion and distress phase of the recovery process helped our family to see that we did have choices about what to keep from our past and what to discard. We became liberated from the darkness and despair we had been living in and moved onto a lighted path headed towards a new beginning.

The more liberated we became, the more issues we found that needed to be addressed.

— We found we needed to learn more about what a healthy relationship was.

— We needed to change habits that were destructive.

— We had to accept the fact that when it comes to depression, struggle is inevitable.

— We learned that when we dealt with our interpersonal relationships, we were bound to make mistakes and that mistake-making was okay.

— We had to accept that discouragement was a part of the process.

— We needed to give ourselves adequate time to deal with and mourn our losses, to cry, to rehash, and to say goodbye. The longer the depression has defined one's life, the more time it takes to grieve.

— We needed to take all the time necessary to sort through all of the inner turmoil we felt.

— We learned how to better structure our time during the day and to allow an hour each evening to work on our relationship issues.

— We each needed to commit ourselves to creating our own sense of self-esteem.

— We needed to show ourselves compassion and to value ourselves and our beliefs.

— We had to stop clamming up, withdrawing and waiting for someone to rescue us.

— We needed to take one day at a time and not worry so much about the future.

— We needed to quit judging ourselves on past mistakes. We learned that we all have the right to be wrong.

— And most important . . . I needed to learn how to let go of Dan's depression and get on with my life.

Section IV

NEW BEGINNINGS

17 | Starting Over

LEAVING THE PAST BEHIND

It was at the very end of our journey through depression that we actually came to the beginning. Once we had ended the old patterns in our relationships and worked through the confusion and distress, we were ready to travel onward into a new beginning where we could begin to implement what we had learned and leave behind the pain-filled past.

Our hope was that the relationships within our family had become better aligned through the therapy process and that, as a family, we had become much more functional and were well on our way to a more harmonious and satisfying way of life.

During this difficult journey from the old life to the new, one of the hardest things to figure out was just exactly when we had passed through the confusion and distress and had reached the threshold of our new beginning. Unfortunately, the three stages—ending, confusion and new beginning—are

155

not easily distinguished. It can be difficult to determine when one is moving from one stage into another. And, of course, there is a lot of overlapping and backtracking.

Throughout our entire life, we all are in a constant state of change but sometimes the beginnings of important phases are not very well marked or fully recognized. Perhaps we first met the person who would become our spouse at a party where all we did was exchange telephone numbers never realizing we would be spending the rest of our lives with each other. When we think about how we first met our best friend or when we chose a major in college or decided to look for a new job, we realize that there was a certain point in our lives when we opened ourselves up to an opportunity of some kind that turned out to be very significant.

Beginnings can be time of great personal growth as well as a time of rebirth for dysfunctional relationships. The foundation for the family's entire future can be laid at this time. Families begin by setting small and attainable goals.

Being able to make decisions and act on them is a major step toward independence and is an important milestone in a family's transition out of depression. Eleanor Roosevelt once spoke about her own life transition at age 35 when "somewhere along the line of development we discover what we really are and then we make our real decision for which we are responsible."

"Make that decision for yourself," she said, "because you can never really live anyone else's life not even your own child's."

Making the transition into a new beginning requires more than perseverance. It also requires an understanding of what it is within us that sabotages us and creates doubt about our ability to be happy

As much as Dan and I wanted to make a new beginning, sometimes our inner voices warned of impending doom if we changed things. While the old life was painful, it was familiar and there was a certain feeling of security in the known. We both had many fears about the unknown. Our relationship was changing and being stretched. There were still some power struggles going on because of the changing dynamics within the family. Who would lead? Would the other family members follow or go their own way? What was now acceptable behavior and what was not?

For families heading towards a new beginning, it is vital that they keep a clear picture of where they want to go and what they want the family relationships to be.

HEALING OUR BROKEN PLACES

We all heal at our own pace. The depressed person may be still in a state of confusion and distress while other family members are entering the new beginning phase; or the family may be in confusion while the depressed person is already at the new beginning. It is desirable for everyone to go through the process together but sometimes it just doesn't work out this way.

Beginnings often create conflict within relationships and some people may even feel a sense of betrayal. "Please don't change," they plead.

A decision to change by a family member may set off danger signals in the person who is depressed. The old rules of the relationship will no longer apply and he or she will have to figure out how to cope with the "new" person.

It's very important at this stage that the person making the change is taking real healing action and not just reacting defensively to the situation or toward the depressed person. Saying things like, "Well, I've had it with you and now I am going to change my life," or making a change in order to hurt someone or to "see that justice is done" is not a true new beginning.

A true new beginning has to start with the ending process, proceed through a period of confusion and distress where things get sorted out, and then advance on to the new choices and the beginning of the new life. This is not an easy process and it does not just happen overnight. We can't avoid the ending phase and just jump into the new beginning. Until we confront the past and resolve its buried conflicts, it will continue to haunt us forever.

Beginnings start within each person. Individuals can

157

only make changes within themselves; they can't make changes in or for anyone else. As the family relationships begin to change, each person can support and enhance the process of healing for the depressed family member but can't expect their efforts to bring picture-perfect results. There are no assurances that everything will turn out okay. By accepting the idea that things must change, families can learn to take this new beginning process one step at a time. Eventually, by working through the depression together, the family will begin to bond in a new and better way.

As Dan and I began to learn about ourselves, we saw how much potential each of us had that we had never tapped into before. I began to try some more assertive behaviors. I would make a decision, jump out and try it, and then go back to what I thought were my old safe ways. Then, I'd jump out and try it again and again. Like a coach on the sidelines, Dale would congratulate our small victories and console us on our defeats.

I learned through our experience that new beginnings were a second chance to rebuild relationships, an opportunity to discover love again, and to reawaken happiness.

The "new beginnings" phase of recovery from depression is a time to:
   – Set goals.
   – Practice new communication methods.
   – Speak positive expressions and love for one another.
   – Establish new boundaries.
   – Forgive each other.
   – Deal with fears as they occur.
   – Have fun together.
   – Spend time together.
   – Try new activities.
   – Let go of the past.

LAYING THE SPOOKS AND GOBLINS TO REST

As the family living in depression moves through the confusion and distress stage and into the new beginning stage, many of the old spooks and goblins are chased out or laid to rest forever.

Family members no longer find themselves protecting or making excuses for the depressed person. In a healthy functioning family, there is no need to do this. The family accepts the depression as an illness like heart disease, diabetes, cancer or some other serious condition that needs to have attention given to it but does not need to be justified.

As a family, we began to feel comfortable just getting on with day-to-day living. Everyone became healthier mentally. We each became more and more responsible for our own actions. The dependent roles began to disappear and our family began to care about one another in healthier ways. Our self-esteem began to grow.

STANDING STRONG WITHOUT FEAR

Our entire family began to have less fear. The kids and I learned how to stand up to Dan and tell the truth about how we felt. We dealt with our fears about Dan threatening or actually committing suicide in a much more realistic way. Dan began to let go of his distorted thinking and the fears that had plagued him for years until he got on the right medication and could see the joy life had to offer. As he gave up his own fears, he was like a child again learning about all the wonders of the world.

As Dan continued to feel better, I began to let go of many of my fears about him. One of my biggest fears was that the depression would come back. Eventually, I came to grips with that fear too. Dan did go through several regressions during the therapy process, but as time went on and he got better and better, my fears began to lessen.

As Gerald Jampolsky points out in his popular book *Love Is Letting Go of Fear,* living without fear is a way of life that opens itself to love. I learned that once I chose to let go of all my fears, the only things left were love and peace of mind.

For families living with depression, a new beginning can stimulate joy and promise in life. As we let go of fear, we began to see some of our previously overwhelming problems as possibilities for growth.

BUILDING, NOT BRUISING—EFFECTIVELY
COPING WITH ANGER

As we became stronger through therapy, we became assertive enough to deal with many of our conflicts before they reached the anger level. We are still human, of course, and we still get mad at each other but now we are much better able to handle our anger without allowing it to become destructive.

Through therapy, we learned new ways of thinking about anger that allowed us to put it in its proper perspective. Anger teaches us much about ourselves. It shows us what is important to us. It shows us what we fear. We learned to ask ourselves, "What am I afraid of and why am I using anger to hide it." It is important to accept the anger, feel it and work through it.

I learned that because I felt anger, I did not necessarily have to use it in a negative way. I could deal with it rationally instead of stuffing it inside and trying to ignore it as I had been doing for many years.

I learned to speak up and discuss some of the "hot topics" with Dan, topics that would have been "hands off" in the past.

As a family, we had to come to grips with the idea that attacking and blaming does not make people change. Anger expresses pain. Dan needed one thing from the rest of the family—acceptance. Although he continued to engage in some unacceptable behaviors and I continued to get angry, I learned how to express my love towards him as well as my pain.

Once we learned new ways to deal with anger and frustration, the potential for violence was virtually eliminated. We learned to take out our anger by beating up a pillow or by taking a long, vigorous walk. We developed arrangements where one of the family members would call for a time-out when they sensed that an argument was escalating too fast. We then took a break from the discussion at hand and let our emotions cool down.

WORKING THROUGH DISCONTENT

There was a turning point where our family began to feel hopeful about our ability to attain realistic goals and fulfill our dreams of a more harmonious family life. In the past, our unrealistic expectations only led to disappointment. We stopped judging and blaming ourselves and each other. No more "he should" or "you should" or "I should have."

By coping with anger more effectively, we found that we lost all desire for revenge. Revenge has no place in a kind and truly loving family environment. It is a deadly, hateful, sick-making tactic.

There were still some lingering feelings of remorse and regret. As with any feeling of grief, the passage of time helped bring us to a place of peace where the pain was less and we decided that what was done was done. We didn't forget the past entirely but we accepted that we had done the best we could with what we knew at the time. Now that we knew more, we could unchain the ropes of the past and create the kind of future we wanted for ourselves and our family.

As Dan began discover his own truths and to believe in himself and his own values again, our family began to recognize and respect him as a person of value. We began communicating without judging each other. We all began to have a feeling of being connected to each other in a much healthier way than we had before as we continued to form new relationships among ourselves.

SAYING HELLO ... SAYING GOODBYE

With all the positive things that are happening at this new beginning stage, one would expect the family members to feel happy about saying hello to the new future. In some cases this is true and the family feels good about who they are and what they are doing. Sometimes, the happiness is short-lived —saying hello to the new means saying goodbye to the old life. Recovery from depression is an uneven process; you feel up and happy for a while and then down and sad for a while. This is natural. The old life is slipping away and even if it was not the best life all the time, it was still something we knew and even cared about.

New beginnings can be a time of joy but also a time of sadness. It's like graduation day. During our school years, we went through hard times and good times, we learned a lot, we have some good memories and some bad ones but on graduation day, we left it all behind and began a new life.

The time of depression may also have served an important purpose for a family. It may have brought issues to the surface to be dealt with that may never have been faced any other way. It may have served the purpose of bringing the entire family closer together. Finding the right cure for the depression is a lot like a graduation from one way of life to another.

I lived a fantasy for a long time believing that once Dan's depression was alleviated, everything would be great. I learned that life with a recovering depressive is not instant bliss. Although many depressed persons do recover there are others who, no matter how hard they try to get better, continue to struggle with their illness for many years.

GAINING MOMENTUM

Recovery from depression is hard work. Family members have to adjust to certain changes in the person recovering from depression. He or she may go through all kinds of personality changes throughout the recovery process—feeling great one day and then lousy the next day. The depressed person may spend a lot of time in therapy or in a support group. At times, the rest of the family, especially the well spouse, may feel neglected and abandoned.

Hard as it is, though, the light generated by recovery is much better for the family than the continuing oppressive darkness of the world of depression in which they have been living. The light leads to happiness and happiness is what all families are searching for.

18 | Creating a Functional Family

GOING FORWARD AND REBUILDING
A TOGETHER FUTURE

Once the depression lifted, as a family, we needed to set new goals that would allow us to move forward in new directions. Finding new meanings and purposes for our lives allowed us to believe in ourselves again. When we began to believe in ourselves, we could then begin to believe in others and in our mutual ability to make positive changes in our family life. Finding new frontiers and setting new goals was a fun process for our family to undertake. We saw that our lives could be so much richer and the opportunities to live life to the fullest so much greater.

Depression had ruled for a long time and when we were finally able to climb out of the pit, the tendency was to run wild for a while. In the excitement of the healing process, we sometimes wanted to do all the things we felt we had been

163

missing because of the depression that had imprisoned us. We wanted to take every family vacation we had ever dreamed about. We wanted to go shopping and buy all the things we had always wanted. We wanted to have a big party, etc. Moderation had to become our watchword at this phase.

One of the best things that happened was that we took some time to process what had happened. We began to enjoy the beauty that was close at home. We walked in our own neighborhood, relaxed in a nearby park, watched a sunset from our own yard, all of which provided joy and serenity with almost no expenditure of funds. Playing with and enjoying our children helped Dan and me rediscover the joy of being a family.

GRINDING IT OUT

Depression caused many problems that we had to cope with long after the illness was gone. One of these was exhaustion. I was exhausted, emotionally, physically and sexually. Throughout the course of the illness, it had seemed to me that everyone was focused on how Dan was doing. It was as if I had been depended upon to provide all the work of keeping things together and now that Dan's recovery was beginning to take place, I had virtually no energy left. Coping with exhaustion became a major battle and I needed to continue getting help even though Dan seemed to be in complete recovery from his illness.

A word of caution to other families—relapses of depression may occur. There may be an episode of depression or a replay of the problems associated with it for some time into the new beginning phase of recovery. When this happened to us, we found we needed to return to therapy for a tune-up now and then. It's a tough ol' world out there sometimes and there is no reason to go through the pain of working out your problems alone. We needed to keep a handle on our problems before they once again got a handle on us. We tried to take care of the future by dealing with the present as it occurred.

Coping with the financial obligations that we had incurred as a result of Dan's depression was another stress.

Depressed people sometimes cannot work and as the bills add up, the collectors are on the phone wanting to know where the payments are. We had to sit down and face this problem realistically, setting a budget, cutting back on some expenses and working out payment plans with the creditors.

COPING STRATEGIES

The following is a list of some coping strategies that I found helpful during the new beginning:

– Don't become over-involved in solving the depressed person's problems or curing the illness for him or her.

– When the depressed spouse starts to get better, accept any offers of help from him or her.

– Set some limits and boundaries on what the family will and will not tolerate—depression or no depression.

– Stop acting the martyr; stop some of the activities that drain the energy and result in exhaustion.

– Each family member should start doing one thing a day that is special—just for him or her.

– Talk with other people about the stress you are feeling.

– Set some personal and family goals and stick to them. Follow your dreams.

– Don't allow the depressed person to drag you into old negative patterns when he or she has a temporary relapse into depression.

– Believe in yourself and your ability to make a difference

– Take as good care of yourself as you take of others.

– Stay current on the new research about depression.

– Attend a support group in your area that deals with this type of mental illness.

All of us, at times, must pick up the pieces and get on with our lives the best way we can. We worked at change together as a family. We also realized that, as individuals, we needed to choose the path that was right for us.

There may be a time during the process of healing when it becomes apparent that a major life change must take place in order for the family to move into a healthier way of life.

Some couples may divorce, some families may move to new places, some spouses may change careers. Whatever the outcome, it is important for each person to realize how much they have learned from their experience with depression.

Depression takes its toll on relationships and, as devastating as this can be, it is important to accept that somehow our lives are richer for having faced what it was that was hurting us and for having the courage to do what was needed to stop the pain. Maturity means accepting the illness, not resenting it.

No one can predict that once we have gone through the healing process, depression will leave our lives forever. Therapy provides a light that can help families living with depression find their way to a better and brighter tomorrow. Shining lights, however, can be expected to attract a few bugs here and there, just like the light on the front porch on a summer night. All the problems and frustrations of dealing with depression are like the bugs trying to get at the light. Family members can glow or fade. They can walk through the bugs or let the bugs "bug" them. Let your own light shine bright and let the bugs fall where they may.

FINDING "THAT HAPPY FAMILY"

Every therapist in the country has his or her own prescription for a happy family. Most of them have dealt with thousands of dysfunctional couples and families and have participated in studies and conferences about family life. A browse through any local bookstore will also tell you that many people are searching for the magic solution that will enable them to achieve family strength, harmony and stability.

After reviewing much of the research on the subject, we came up with a formula for an ideal family that seemed possible to achieve.

1. We tried to work together as a team and we began to believe that we could do anything or be anything we wanted to be or do.

Dan and I tried to be more supportive of each other and yet not sacrifice ourselves in order to make the relationship work. We allowed change to happen and we adapted as needed.

We worked at establishing an openness in the family that allowed us to be comfortable accepting assistance from the outside world when we needed it. Because of the depression, we had tended to try to close ourselves off from the outside. It was vital in the new beginning phase of recovery that we opened up to help from the outside in terms of support and understanding, particularly from the medical community.

2. Dan and I developed specific personal boundaries that would allow each of us room to stand together or alone and still feel secure.

3. We spent time talking and laughing together and tried not to send any mixed messages to each other. We learned some good problem-solving skills that allowed us enough room to disagree and we tried harder to handle our disagreements in more positive ways.

4. We stopped struggling for control and tried to build our marriage relationship on a base of equality.

5. We are learning that it's O.K. to display a wide and varied range of emotions. We can allow ourselves to experience great joy and great despair. We don't need to be afraid to show anger and yet we can have a lot of fun together We try to handle disappointments and setbacks by freely expressing how we feel. We don't judge each other's responses to problems and we don't deny anyone the right to feel. We try to be creative when it comes to solving crisis situations and we accept problems in life as a learning experience, not a punishment.

6. We stopped being so dependent on each other. Each of us is a whole person with or without the other people in the family. We need not feel threatened by close loving relationships. We should be able to tell each other how we feel, not tell others how they should feel. Each person should believe that however strong their grief at the loss, if the other person died they would still be a whole person

7. We used a win-win problem-solving style. We truly listened to one another and when we came to a place where there was no settlement, we tried to find a way that everyone could win.

167

8. We worked at creating a loving environment, making our home warm and comfortable. Mementoes, photographs, children's hand-drawn pictures on the fridge, all say "this is our home and we are a family."

9. We began to prize rituals—Christmas, Thanksgiving, other holidays, birthdays, weddings, funerals. These help to unify families and a unified family is a priceless treasure in life.

10. We began to share a similar belief about our personal views on a spiritual level. Although we recognize that this life does not not last forever, we relish it and are willing to enjoy it as long as it lasts.

In the new beginning stage, families who have been living in depression need to have some kind of a spiritual connection to each other and a shared vision about the future.

19 | Seeking a Higher Power

SPIRITUAL BANKRUPTCY

As a family member living with someone who suffered from depression, I found there were many days and nights of despair when I thought, "Why me? What did I do to deserve this?" I had a husband who was constantly down in the dumps. I was taking care of my kids, going to college trying to make something of my life and every day was a struggle.

Putting Dan's depression into some kind of perspective was not possible until I found my own sense of spirituality and created a sense of purpose and meaning to my life. I had no real religious training growing up. I went with the neighbor kids to church once in a while. I think it instilled a certain sense of good moral values in me but I never felt connected to a higher power.

As an adult, living with a depressed spouse, I was working and trying to take each day as it came but, day by day, I was slipping into my own state of depression. I was tired of

169

Dan and his demands. I was feeling overwhelmed by the work required for my final semester of school. I was getting ready to graduate and Dan was not taking his medication. He was falling apart again, not going to work and spending most of his time in bed.

Graduation day came and, in many ways, it was a disaster. My parents were angry with me, my relatives were upset because each group of them felt I hadn't spent enough time with them. I was sad to leave all the wonderful friends I had met in college. I didn't know what I was going to do in the future.

Finally, about two weeks after my college graduation, I got up one morning and everything snapped. Dan was taking the kids out for the day and, after I sent all of them out the door, I walked into the kitchen, sat down and fell apart. I wrote Dan a note telling him that I just could not stay in the house that weekend and that I had to get away for a while. I needed to find out who I was and where I belonged. I grabbed my purse, a notebook, my car keys and an apple, walked out the door, got into my car and left.

I headed towards the Oregon Coast. I had never done anything like this in my life and I had no idea about whether or not I could follow through with it. It was 500 miles to the ocean and I had never gone anywhere this far alone. It was raining very hard and, as I drove, I had to face a lot of my own fears. I didn't know how to read a map. I had no money, only a credit card. I had to think about stopping to get gas, buy food, and deal with all the other things that might come up on a 500-mile-long car trip. I cried a lot.

It was Memorial Day weekend so the traffic was very heavy. It was raining hard and the highways were like ice rinks. I was in a state of high anxiety. The farther I got away from home, the more I cried. I began to realize how completely I had let my life be overrun by Dan's depression. I had never given myself the opportunity to separate from it long enough to find out who I was. As I drove on, I became aware of how spiritually bankrupt I really was.

I realized that I was experiencing profound grief. I felt very sad about all the parts of my life that I had lost and even

170

for what I had never had. I had given up so much of what I believed in and so much of who I was in order to try to live with someone who was depressed.

As I drove through downtown Portland, I looked at families in other cars and wondered how many of them were living with secrets, how many of them were living with the pain and hell of depression, and how many of them would ever admit it or go for help.

I drove on in to McMinnville and decided to stay there for the night. It was graduation night at McMinnville College and everyone was partying and driving up and down the streets whistling and waving. People were hugging each other in the convenience store where I stopped to pick up some food. The kids were telling each other how sorry they were to leave one another. It was the kind of celebration that I had hoped to have when I had graduated two weeks earlier. Watching these kids now, I wanted to go up to them and tell them I had just graduated too and share some of their joy. Surrounded by all this happiness, I felt even sadder.

I went to my hotel room and I sat in the dark and I looked at the window and thought, "I hope I'm doing the right thing, I hope that by the time I get done with this trip, I will know what I can believe in."

I wanted to know that, not only had I graduated from college, I also had made some big steps in learning about life.

When I got up the next morning, I could see it was going to be a picture-perfect day. The previous night had been the first one I had spent entirely alone in years and I woke up with a real sense of inner peace.

I listened to classical music as I drove through miles and miles of green, lush farmland and through the mountains and the forests partly hidden by the fog. It was spectacularly beautiful all the way to the coast. As I came over a mountain pass and dropped down towards the coast, I was amazed at how quiet and serene it was.

I stopped the car, got out and walked over to the beach and just stood there with the gentle wind blowing against me. I felt as one with the ocean and the wind. It was the safest feeling I have ever had. I felt a sense of peace that I had never experienced before in my life. There was no logical reason for me to feel such a sense of peace. I was 500 miles from home, doing something I had never done before, putting my marriage and my future totally on the line. My life was in shambles and yet, here I stood on a beach next to a busy highway and feeling so peaceful and in touch with a higher power.

I walked back up to the car and continued my drive down the coast. I looked in awe at the beauty of everything. As I realized I could believe in my own instincts, I began to totally enjoy myself. I went to a small motel and checked in. My room was full of antiques. It had a little fireplace and a deck that overlooked the ocean. I made myself some hot tea and sat down and started to write about everything that I had felt on this trip. I poured all of my emotions, all of my hopes, dreams and fears out onto the paper.

While I was writing, I got an idea. I went into town and bought some black balloons. I went back to the motel and wrote for two hours about all of the pain, all my fears, all my difficulties, and all the things I needed to let go of so that I could move forward and get on with my life. I used different sheets of paper for the different topics like: depression, why I was so angry at it, why I needed to let go of it and what I was going to do once it was gone; Dan and his problems; things that Dale had said and that had made me very angry, even though they were said to help me grow.

It was very hard work. I had to allow myself to feel a lot of pain. I had to look over a lot of resentment I had stored about things I wished I had done but never had. Once I had finished writing, I very carefully rolled the papers up and tied each one with a black ribbon to one of the blown-up balloons.

As the sun was almost setting, I carried all the balloons down to the beach. There was a family sitting on the sand and I wondered if I should wait until they left to do what I needed to do. I was so overcome with emotion, I just couldn't stop at that point. I walked a little way down the beach and as I looked at the sunset, I tried to come to grips with letting go all of the pain that I had carried around for so many years.

It was a difficult decision because I had held on to it for so long, it was almost like a security blanket. I was afraid that

172

if I let it go, I would forget and it would happen to me again and again and I would get myself into the same situations over and over.

I stood out on the beach and literally talked to my higher power. I said, "I need to know what to do, I can't do this alone anymore, I don't know what to do."

Suddenly, I got a very strong feeling that something was telling me, "Let them go and let it be. Let them go and let it be." I turned toward the ocean and let all the balloons go.

At first, it seemed that they weren't going to rise and I thought, "Oh, no. I've just driven 500 miles to do this and now they are not going up and they are not going away."

I started yelling at the balloons, "Rise! Rise! I don't want you here anymore! I don't want to hurt anymore!" As the balloons finally began to rise up in the air over the coast, I sat down on a piece of driftwood and I cried and cried and cried. It felt as if that part of my life was truly over, it was finished and I would never have to go back to that terrible pain again. It was the final ending to the entire therapy process.

I sat there for a long time. Then, I walked back toward the motel with tears running down my face but with such a sense of relief that it was finally over and I had let go of so many things.

Just then, I looked down and saw that a net had washed up on the shore practically at my feet. I picked it up and thought how strange that this net should wash up just as I was walking by. I could see a woman walking towards me and I hoped she wouldn't come over to talk to me because I had been crying and knew I looked awful. I still felt bad and I hoped she would just leave me alone!

I tried to move off to one side to avoid her but she kept right on coming towards me. She asked me if I was grieving something. I told her I was and she said, "I want you to know that my family and I were sitting there and we watched you come down with those black balloons and stand out there and let them go and we want you to know that it was the most beautiful thing we have ever seen. It touched our hearts very deeply and we felt very connected to you and your pain."

She said they had taken pictures of me and asked me if

she could send one to her son. He was in jail in Portland and they didn't know if he was going to get out. He was very depressed and suicidal and she said the picture might be the one thing that could help him to hold on until he could get out.

It suddenly dawned on me that I was still holding the net I had picked up. I told the woman, "I drove 500 miles to get here to this place. I needed to come here and to let go of all my pain. I would like you to do something for me. I want you to mail this net to your son and tell him it is from me."

She looked puzzled as she took the net from my arms. I said, "Tell your son that no matter what happens, no matter how bad it gets, that underneath all of us there is an invisible safety net. It is there for us when we fall and when our loved ones fall. Together, we all hold the net."

She looked at me and began to cry. We stood there, two strangers on the beach, hugging each other and trying to help one another through our two different kinds of pain that neither one of us truly understood. I realized at that moment how important it is that we lean on each other and help each other through the really hard times.

The woman turned and walked away down the beach holding the net and even though I never saw her or heard from her again, I knew that we had truly touched each other's lives and that we were both on that beach together for a reason.

As I watched the setting sun drop beneath the horizon, I knew that I was on my way to becoming much more spiritually reconnected and much more in tune with my purpose in being. I went back up to my room and sat out on the deck looking out over the ocean.

As I sat there taking in the beauty of nature around me, I became aware of the tremendous force of all the water hitting rocks. I thought about the kind of energy it takes to create the swell of water that surrounded me. I felt myself a part of that force. It was an awakening for me that I had needed all of my life. The force was beginning to show me how to create new paths for my life. I did not have to allow my life to be controlled by my husband's depression. My spiritual connection was mine alone. I could use that connection to find inner solace and support. I could create a place inside me where I could feel peace in the face of all of the chaos that depression had caused in all our lives.

As the stars came out that night, I sat and watched the ocean. It was so calming and so peaceful yet so big and so powerful. I thought, "How can I take that strength and incorporate it into my own life. How can I be strong, secure, feel safe, help my family members feel safe and, along with that strength, also have a sense of peace?"

The more I thought about it, the clearer it became. All I had to do was make the decision to live my life that way. To live it very peacefully, very securely and to rely on a great deal of faith that as a family, we could survive as individuals no matter how bad it got. We would make it. Even if Dan and I decided to end our relationship, we could still come away from the experience better people than when we started.

I spent the next day sitting on the beach reflecting about everything that had happened in the last 11 years with our family's struggle with depression. I began to understand the importance of being quiet. We cannot receive inspiration if we are busy talking all the time. The inspiration can't get through.

I meditated, prayed and felt a real sense of a new beginning. As I continued to release all the emotions and pain that I had felt throughout my marriage, my hurts began to heal. I enjoyed an intimacy with a force bigger than myself that had created the pounding ocean waves. I was surrounded by vast amounts of untouched sand and I was blessed by magnificent sunsets that included every color of the rainbow.

When it was time to go, I headed back home with a new perspective about my life and about the future. I realized that on my spiritual journey, I had discovered much about how I wanted to live. I made a commitment to turn all the pain and fear that depression had brought to our lives into peace and love. I came home with more compassion for Dan than I had ever had before. I had discovered what unconditional love felt like. I had been immersed in it as I walked on the beach and made the decision to incorporate it into my life.

BALANCING ACT

Once I decided that my purpose in life was to love myself and others and to learn and to grow, I finally understood my own spiritual path. I couldn't fix Dan's depression but I could love him, and show him the compassion that he truly needed.

For those of us who live with mental illness on a daily basis, it is vital that we come to terms with our own spirituality. Sometimes we get angry and feel that if we are living righteously, we should be guaranteed an existence free of tragedy and serious difficulties. If we never experience misery, we can never appreciate the happiness in our life. Tragedy and difficulty are part of our mortal lives. If we are willing to allow a higher power to share some of our burden and help us in our struggle, it can lessen our feelings of isolation and shame and strengthen our spirit.

Releasing our pain to a higher power also can free us from self-pity. As we turn the focus of our attention away from our own pain and our own problems and towards helping others, we can experience great joy. There is no easy formula for gaining a spiritual perspective, but if we nurture a spiritual side of ourselves, we have a much greater chance of success for a new beginning in our lives.

MIND, BODY, SPIRIT

Many therapists are beginning to practice a therapeutic process that involves mind, body and spirit which helps their clients to create an inner balance and a feeling of wholeness. The impact of getting in touch with one's spiritual nature can lead to significant life changes.

People who suffer from depression may be very devout spiritual people who just plain cannot cope anymore. They just don't have the interest or the energy inside themselves to rekindle the light of spirituality that is almost burned out. We all have a higher purpose and we all deserve to have a life full of peace and happiness, but depressed people are not at a place where they can do that.

Some people become very judgmental towards those who

suffer from depression. They see this illness as almost a crisis of faith and that is the way they sometimes approach a depressed person. Because of their lack of understanding of the illness, they may react to depressed people with a sense of gloom and doom. They tend to focus on all the negative things that a depressed person is doing and they become over-zealous at giving advice. They tell the depressed person to "just get your life right with God, then all of this depression will lift."

This kind of remark shows a great lack of understanding of depression and its biological causes. As much as the depressed person may want his problems to be solved by increased spirituality, it seems not to provide the entire answer for many people. It is important that we each find our own sense of spirit but we can't impose our desires and beliefs on others.

A SENSE OF PEACE

Our spiritual connections, whatever they are, are our own. They are vital to our peace of mind. In a world where, day in and day out, headlines scream at us of murders, rapes, child abuse and other manifestations of the darker side of human nature, our spirituality is what keeps us believing in the goodness of people in the face of so much despair.

Everyone comes to his or her own spiritual connection differently. I was fortunate to find a place where I felt I could commune with my higher power. Some people find their spirituality in a church, others find it at the top of a mountain. It doesn't matter how one finds that spiritual connection, it matters that we have it to sustain us through the rough times.

Spirituality is so important to our sense of balance and yet, when we are living with depression, it is an area of our lives that tends to get put low on the list of our priorities. We have so many demands on our time that it becomes impossible to fit everything in. Spirituality tends to be one of those things we put off the most. I realized through my healing experience at the Oregon coast that the times I needed my spiritual connection the most were the times I put it at the bottom of the list. That was when chaos reigned and life was the toughest.

Like recovery from depression, spirituality is a process. It takes a lot of time and a lot of effort to find a place that is safe and secure to connect at a soul level with a higher being. It is a strength that can sustain families through the rough times and a light that shines through the darkness of the worst days.

Spirituality in our lives brings us a sense of peace. The more chaos we are experiencing, the more we need our spirituality to provide us with that sense of peace in our lives and within our hearts. Spirituality is like good insurance. It is there when families need it and it will help take care of them and bring them safely through the hard times.

20 | Forgiving: Building Bridges Instead of Walls

"If you will not forgive someone for what they have done wrong . . . don't ever expect anyone to forgive you."
                                    Lewis B. Smedes

Hefty Cinch Sacks are the kind of trash bags I use at home. I like Hefty Cinch Sacks because they are strong and sturdy and they hold a lot of trash. If you pour a lot of messy stuff in them they won't leak and it doesn't matter what you do to them, they rarely let the garbage come out.

Those Hefty Cinch Sacks remind me a lot of myself— strong, sturdy and capable of holding a lot of trash.

There is something important about trash. It tells us a lot about ourselves. Are we taking care of ourselves? Is the trash full of fast-food wrappers or does it contain steak bones? Are we taking care of our environment? Does the trash bag hold raked-up leaves? Are the recyclables separated? Our trash bags reflect the changes taking place in our lives.

If we forget to take out the trash, it begins to take us over. It spills out onto the kitchen floor, it fills up the garage and starts to smell bad. Because of the smell, we cannot forget it's there until the garbage collector finally takes it away. Once it is gone, we think Hallelujah!! The house looks cleaner and smells a lot better and we feel better too. After a couple of days we never really think about what we've thrown away.

Like me, many people who live with depression become surrounded by trash. This stash of trash is a result of many years of emotional pain and an accumulation of bitter memories that we store away as if our minds were giant Hefty bags. Just like the trash that is overflowing in the kitchen and taking over the garage, all of the emotional pain and garbage that we have stashed begins to overflow and control who we are and how we act.

We keep score. We think about how many times we have been hurt by the depressed person and we decide to catalog those hurts in our minds so that we can make sure they never happen again.

This system works really well. Not only do we have all of the "dastardly deeds" piling up in our mental trash bag, but they are also cataloged in such a way that we can find them at any time and we can pull them out and look at them again and again and again. More importantly, we can use them to justify anything rotten that we ourselves do because, after all, the other person did something to us first and we were just getting even.

We get even by judging and blaming. We know how unfair our life is and how unjustly we have been treated by the depressed person. We know how cruel he or she has been. We know that if he or she "would just get better, our lives would be great . . . no more problems." We attribute most of the conflict and the hassles in our lives to the actions of the depressed family member.

And we carry our bag of the judging and blaming trash around with us. We think we have it under control but sometimes the bag gets too heavy and starts to overwhelm us. All of this emotional trash begins to stifle us. In order to create new beginnings we need to get rid of it so our house will "smell" better.

180

Through forgiveness, we can dump the garbage out one hurt at a time.

Forgiveness is tough. No one can teach us exactly how to do it. It's a choice but if we choose to forgive and let all of the wrongs disappear, we will be able to throw out the trash and forget what it was we threw away. We can tear down the walls that are preventing the real intimacy that we long for. Once the walls come tumbling down, we can begin to build a bridge that leads us back to love and caring.

"What is forgiveness anyway?" I asked Dale during an intense therapy session. We had been discussing all of the anger and resentment that I had been feeling about Dan's depression. I had been doing a lot of blaming and judging and trying to figure out why my life was in such a shambles. It was hard for me to understand why I was still mad. I felt as though Dan and his illness were waging war against me and I could not fight back because I had no weapons. Fighting any mental illness is like going into a battle without ammunition.

So, in the heat of discussing all of this in therapy, Dale said, "Why don't you try forgiving?" I was outraged. I was the victim of all of this emotional abuse. I had a right to be angry. "I am not going to forgive him. Look at all of these terrible things he has done to me!" I said defiantly.

"I'm not talking about forgiving Dan, I'm talking about forgiving yourself."

I was stunned. I sat there in thought. (Like other good therapists, Dale has a way of uttering one simple sentence that can turn your whole train of thought around.)

"Myself?" I thought, "What is he talking about? What have I done?"

I just didn't know what to say and Dale waited for me to think it through and then said, "You need to work through your own pain and forgive yourself for all of the pain that you have caused in this relationship. You need to dump out all the guilt you feel about not being able to save Dan from this illness. Then, we can talk about forgiving Dan and his illness."

"What? What? I'm not sure I understand what you're saying. Are you saying that the answer to all of this anger is to forgive? I don't want to forgive, I want to go out and blow up a building or something. I'm not even religious and you want me to forgive? What is forgiveness anyway, Dale?" I asked.

Dale sat back in his chair and smiled. "It's a good way to dump your trash and get on with your life."

I left the therapy session that night in a real state of confusion. How could forgiveness be a part of living with depression? What was he talking about, dumping the trash? I was wrapped up in emotion. I did not understand why I had to be the one to forgive. After all, I was the wronged woman, wasn't I?

I thought and thought and thought about it and decided I needed to learn more about forgiveness. I headed out to the local bookstore and picked up a copy of Lewis B. Smede's book *Forgive and Forget: Healing the Hurts We Don't Deserve.* That book literally turned my life around.

It is an easy-to-read book that describes in a simple and understandable format the stages and the elements of the forgiving process:

> We hurt.
> We hate.
> We heal ourselves.
> We come together.

We hurt. Because I lived with depression, I constantly got myself into emotional situations where I ended up getting hurt. It hurts to be ignored. It hurts to be emotionally violated. The hurt was unfair and gut-wrenching.

Many times Dan didn't think or play fair in our relationship. It hurt to see our children somewhat abandoned and left to fend for themselves because their parents were so busy dealing with an illness. It wasn't fair that Dan's problems affected so many other lives so severely. It hurt to be demeaned in front of other people. All of the things that happened were devastating to the kids and me. It was very hard to forgive.

The unfairness of this illness led us into the second stage in the forgiveness process.

We hate. Hate was a hard word for me to accept. I was always taught that you were not supposed to hate anyone. Hate was a four-letter-word in my vocabulary. But, when I got really honest with myself, I had to admit that there were times in the course of Dan's illness when I experienced hateful feelings toward him. Most of this hate was the result of feeling betrayed and mentally brutalized.

Hate is a form of inner violence. It drove Dan and me apart and we became consumed with rage. Hate and love were like the two ends of a see-saw going up and down with every up and down in our relationship. We both loved and hated each other at different times throughout the process.

I thought I really hated Dan for all the terrible things he had done. There was a time when I wanted the worst for Dan because I was hurt so badly. I wanted him to experience all the painful feelings I had experienced. I wanted him to pay in full for my pain.

Projecting my hatred of the illness onto Dan was not unusual. We hate most painfully the people that we love the most passionately.

Finally I realized that I did not hate Dan—what I really hated was the illness and the way it made him act. I hated the depression. Depression caused him to do the things he did and if the depression was out of his life, he would return to the same wonderful man I had married.

In order to live in a productive way, I had to begin to deal with my feelings of hate. Hate that is lodged against another person is very hard to heal. I had to learn to focus my hate on the illness of depression instead of on Dan. Once the symptoms of depression went away, the hate went away too.

The payoff for hating Dan was that I had someone to blame. I could pronounce the guilty sentence over Dan's head. I sat as the judge and jury condemning him to a life of repentance. I was being as unfair as I perceived him to be. I needed to forgive Dan in order to cleanse my own soul of hate and allow the healing to begin.

We heal ourselves. Forgiveness involves making a separation between the person who has hurt us and the illness. Forgiving allowed me to look at the sad and lonely and needy person Dan was and to recognize that he could not control how he acted and felt because of the depression that had taken him prisoner.

I began to change my perceptions about the past by taking another look at memories. I didn't forget what had happened but, as a result of my willingness to forgive, my perceptions about what had happened in the past began to change.

When I accepted that depression was the real problem in our marriage, I decided to write off all the past hurts. What Dan did two years ago or three years ago or six months ago became irrelevant to how I felt about him here and now.

We came together. Through this process the person who gained the most from the forgiving process in our relationship was me. When the mortar of hate crumbled, the walls I had built to protect myself began to fall. The walls needed to be cleared away before the bridge-building that would solidify our family could begin.

Bridges must be constructed on a foundation of truth. Each person must be able and willing to say what he feels inside and what kind of new relationships he or she wants in the future. Then each must accept responsibility for the pain he has caused others in the past. The pain-giver needs to recognize the unfairness of what he has done and he needs to hear from loved ones how much they have been hurt.

Because no two people ever remember the past exactly the same, it is not unusual to disagree on many points related to a hurtful incident that happened in the past. The depressed person should at the very least acknowledge that he has indeed caused pain and he must try to understand the hurt that family members felt. Until this is done, other family members may not be willing to try to go through the forgiving process.

Lewis B. Smede says, for alienated partners trying to build a bridge back to each other, "it requires a promise made and a promise meant to keep. Both partners must promise not to intentionally hurt each other again and have every truthful intention of keeping that promise."

When we are hurt, we struggle to try to understand why. Maybe even after we start healing, we still don't truly understand what happened. But we don't need to have all the answers to all the whys before we begin the forgiving process.

184

We don't even need to have the person who hurt us in our lives at the time we begin it. Forgiveness is something we can do alone.

Forgiving is not forgetting. We can't forget until we have worked through the entire forgiving process. As Smede writes in his book, "If you forget, you will not forgive at all. You need to forgive precisely because you have not forgotten about what someone did. Your memory has kept the pain alive long after the actual hurt has stopped. The memory is the reason you need to forgive in the first place."

We can forget trivial hurts, but we get into trouble when we push significant pain out of our minds and our memories. When we don't deal with the bad things that happen to us, we end up stuffing them into that Hefty sack of our subconscious mind where we think they can be controlled and taken care of. Forgetting pain becomes a game of "Russian Roulette." You never know when some old deeply buried hurt will jump out and shoot you down.

When families who have been living with depression begin putting the pieces of their lives back together and try to work through the forgiving process, they sometimes find this a way to excuse the depressed person for the "bad" behavior of the past. There is a difference, however, between forgiving someone and excusing him. We forgive people for things we have blamed them for. We excuse depressed people because we understand mental illness caused them to act they way they did.

This understanding may make it a little easier to excuse the problems that the illness caused, but it is still very difficult to forgive the depressed person who has been the instrument of so much pain to the family. We can begin the process by forgiving ourselves first.

The Bible tells us to "love thy neighbor as thyself." My new motto is "forgive thy neighbor as thyself." We all have faults and all the family members may have contributed significantly to the problems that have occurred since the onset of the depression.

Forgiving the past and letting it go allows all of us to dump our trash, heal our wounds and get on with our new beginning.

It is important to remember that the forgiving process is just that, a process. And it takes time. We can't expect to forgive someone something and then, like magic, everything is okay. We need to allow time for the process to work and time to rebuild our family relationships. Depending on the severity of the depression, it can take weeks, months, and even years to work through all of the emotional injuries we have experienced because of the illness.

It helps sometimes to put ourselves in the depressed person's shoes and to realize that no matter how hard it has been for spouses and other family members to deal with the illness, it has been much worse for him or her living alone in the black hole of depression.

Forgiveness should not be used as a superiority trap. If we choose to forgive someone, it does not mean that we are superior to them, it means that we are no longer willing to carry all of the anger and frustration that we have felt towards that person and that we have decided we want to live a more whole, a more loving, a more satisfying existence.

21 | Starting Over

In some respects, I have benefitted from our family's struggle with depression. I have learned a tremendous amount about life, love, happiness and mostly about myself. Against some pretty overwhelming odds, I managed to graduate from college, earn a master's degree, write two books and open my own training and consulting business while still being a wife, a mom and a depression researcher. Dan's illness complicated our lives, but learning to cope with it enriched us.

It was frustrating and difficult for me at times to stay with him and to stand by him. I never forget that behind that monster mask created by the depression, there really is a kind, caring and wonderful human being. For me, accepting Dan's illness was the most important step in the entire recovery process. I no longer use my energy to deny the illness and I have given up unrealistic expectations for Dan or for myself.

Another important step for me was accepting that, in order to live with depression, I had to learn how to adapt and become more flexible. I had to accept the fact that my plans for family activities were subject to change or modification. I now do the things I want to do. I have become much more independent.

My children also have learned to cope with the ups and downs of depression. They still meet with a therapist as needed to work on problems related to the illness.

Being able to adapt to whatever each day brings, to love and to forgive has helped us through the bad times and continues to help us deal with this illness.

I have learned to live in truth. Living in truth allows us all to discover how much strength we have to share with one another and with those outside our family.

I have learned to detach myself from the illness and, even if Dan is depressed and unhappy, I don't have to feel the same way. I know that happiness does not just happen. It is a choice, an action we can decide to take or not. I now take responsibility for my own joy.

PLEASE HOLD YOUR APPLAUSE
UNTIL THE END

I am learning to take life one day at a time. While we have made tremendous progress in restructuring our lives, we have not yet won our battle with depression. We must work at it every day.

There are some great days and there are still some horrible days. I never know what is going to happen next. When the illness takes over, I watch Dan fade away like a shadow into the night. Without cause or reason, a person I don't know wearing the mask of depression comes to replace him.

I wish I could end this book by saying "and they lived happily ever after." But our family is not the Brady Bunch, we are not images on the television screen. We are a real, living and breathing family still struggling with the effects of depression on our lives. The tears still flow but we hold on, hoping that someday researchers will find a cure for the depression that has caused so much pain for our family and for so many other families living with this illness.

Dale and I have written this book because we wanted to provide a safety net for other families struggling with depression. In many ways, writing this book has reinforced my own safety net. Telling this story has opened my heart to the problems we all face in coping with this illness. When Dan's depression escalates, I reread much of what I have written to remind myself how far we have come on our journey through depression and how much hope there is for the future. Coping with depression is never easy. It is a complex illness that affects millions of us every year.

Standing together families can support and encourage each other and shine a light onto the darkness of depression.

Together we all hold the net.

– **The End** –

ABOUT THE AUTHORS:

John Sinclair

KELLIE BRANSON, M.S., has a degree in Communication and a Masters degree in Instructional/ Performance Technology. She currently consults and conducts training seminars for business and industry on human relations issues. She and Dale Babcock have recently designed a seminar program for corporations entitled "Employee Depression: The Silent Killer of American Business."

John Sinclair

DALE BABCOCK, M.S., is the founder of the Institute for Counseling in Meridian, Idaho He is a licensed professional counselor and has over 20 years of counseling experience. He conducts workshops on family issues as well as conflict management and communication workshops for business. He is a member of the National Certified Counselors Association.

We were assisted by:

JEAN TERRA, a free-lance writer/editor with over 20 years of experience in a wide variety of subject matter. She has been a journalist, magazine editor, a publicist and a press secretary and speech writer to a former Governor of Idaho. She is currently living and working in Boise.